STORIES FROM NATURE

Thirty-one Animal Tales

by Jane Werner Watson • illustrated by Gerda Muller

 GOLDEN PRESS • NEW YORK
Western Publishing Company, Inc.
Racine, Wisconsin

Contents

AT THE EDGE OF TOWN the houses stand farther and farther apart, with gardens and meadows and fields between and the deep woods beyond. There the worlds of People and Nature meet.

8

The mothers and fathers think they own the houses with their lawns and gardens, all for themselves and their families. Really, though, they share them with many neighbors from the nearby meadows and woods.

Woods and Meadows

In the cool of the morning, dewdrops sparkle on green leaves. Then the rabbits who live in the bramble hedge at the edge of the meadow hop to the vegetable garden. They come for a breakfast of tender young plants. It never occurs to them that they might not be welcome.

All day long birds fuss and twitter about. In the spring they are busy choosing spots for building nests. Some like to build on

9

branches of trees or in thick bushes deep in the woods. Others like the shelter of thick-leaved, twisting vines. Still others like to build their nests close to people, under the shade of eaves or on sturdy rafters.

Whatever spot they choose, the birds consider it their very own, just as the people do. They are ready to fight other birds for their home place.

In the early summer the birds are busy raising their young. In the autumn most of them fly south to warmer forests. But a few stay on in the woods and meadows. Through the cold winter they especially welcome bits of bread and suet and tasty seeds the people in the houses put out for them.

Field mice live in small underground burrows. People do not put out food for them. The mice come out at night, though, to search for supplies. If the hunt leads them into a house, they feel they have a right to anything they find. They like to fill their cheeks with seeds to carry home for their babies. Or with their small sharp teeth they nibble holes in paper and cloth to provide soft lining for their nests.

There are insects, too, by the hundreds and thousands. They make their homes in trees, bushes and flowering plants or even under the ground. Some insects creep, some crawl, some hop about, some fly. They creep or crawl or hop or fly right into a house if they can. It never occurs to them that their world might belong to someone else.

Where the tall dark shape of the woods towers against the sky beyond the meadow, other birds and animals make their homes. They drink at the stream that wanders through the woods and out across the meadow, and then curves toward the town. Wherever they find food that suits them, they stop to nibble.

Some woods animals eat bugs and grubs. Some, like beavers, eat leaves and twigs. Others scoop up fish from the stream, or dig up tender roots with their paws. There are woods folk that prefer the ripe plump berries that grow on woodland plants to any other food.

Hunters of the woods, like the fox and the owl, eat small animals. If they did not, there would be so many small animals that none of them could find enough to eat.

If you wish to meet these dwellers in the woods, you must walk very quietly through their world. A jay may chatter at you from a high branch. A rabbit may watch you, still as can be, from the shelter of a thick, low bush. A squirrel may scamper from tree to tree above your head, chattering as he goes.

Many of the woods folk are so shy, though, that only if you sit very still will you get to see them. If you are very quiet, a porcupine may waddle across the path near you and slowly climb to his nest in a tree. Or a mother deer may step cautiously out of a thicket. She will flick her ears this way and that, listening for danger. She will lift her soft nose to sniff the breeze and turn her big brown eyes from side to side. Only then, if she doesn't sense any danger, will she step gracefully out into the clearing. And behind her may come a slender spotted fawn.

To see foxes, raccoons and other night-lovers, you must stay in the woods—or nearby—as the last daylight fades from the evening sky. It is then that these hunters venture out after food. They may come across the meadow close to the people's houses, if all is quiet there. But it is deep in the woods that many of them make their homes, summer, winter, spring and fall. Are you willing to pack a picnic lunch and walk quietly down woodland paths? If you are, you can visit these friends at home.

10

A Spring Surprise

BETWEEN THE WIDE GREEN MEADOW and the big woods runs a hedgerow of bramble bushes. To humans these bushes seem rough and prickly. Their sharp stickers catch and tear trousers and shirts; they scratch arms and legs. So humans avoid the bramble patch and take the long path around it into the big woods. But to the rabbits the bramble patch is home. Its prickers and stickers keep them safe. Its thick mesh of leafy branches shuts out the hot sun.

Down in the soft shade of the rabbits' home under the bramble bushes, three small bunny rabbits sat one spring day, twiddling their whiskers.

"I'm hungry," said Michael Bunny with a sigh.

"So am I," said Bridget Bunny. "Remember the clover blossoms we nibbled yesterday out in the meadow?"

"Yes," said Michael, "but the farmer and his son are working in the meadow today, cutting the clover for hay."

"Remember the tender young lettuce leaves we found in the garden?" said Bridget. Her small pink nose quivered at the delicious thought.

"Yes," said Michael, "but the farmer's wife is working in the garden today."

"Well," said Christopher Bunny, "you would never have found the clover patch or the lettuce rows if I had not gone exploring. I suppose that is what I must do again."

"Oh, good!" said Bridget Bunny.

"Best of luck," said Michael, stretching his hind legs lazily. "When you find something tasty, let us know."

Then they both settled back on their soft beds of nice dusty leaves for a pleasant midday nap.

Christopher Bunny made his way out of the bramble patch. When he reached the sunlight at the edge of the woods, he sat very still for a moment. His bright eyes looked this way and that. His soft nose sniffed the breeze. He thumped one hind foot thoughtfully.

"All is well," he said to himself. "Now which way shall I try first?"

He thought of the brook that ran through the big woods, all brown and gold in the dappled green shade. He thought of the crisp and spicy watercress that grew beside the brook where a cold spring of water bubbled out of the bank. At the thought, his whiskers twitched.

Lippity clippity into the woods Christopher Bunny hopped. Soon he could hear the burble of the brook as it danced along through the dappled shade. There were other sounds in the deep woods, though— not the call of the jays or the harsh caws of the crows, not the hungry squeaking of baby birds in their nests, but strange voices.

Christopher Bunny crept forward carefully, moving in the lacy shadows of ferns that
12

curled among the tree roots. At last, from behind a big oak tree, he could see the brook, brown in the shadows and gold in the sun. He could see the crisp green leaves of watercress on the bank.

But between Christopher Bunny and the watercress sat People. They were in a circle on the green moss, eating a picnic lunch. There were two great big people and two middle-sized ones, and one not so very much larger than the bunny himself.

Now some rabbits are afraid of people. Not Christopher! He was a brave explorer. Also, his soft bunny nose was twitching with delight at the smell of food.

Very quietly Christopher Bunny crept closer and closer to the people. Being a bright bunny as well as a brave one, he kept his whiskers stiffly alert for danger.

Soon Christopher was very close to the picnic. And what do you suppose happened then? The smallest of the people, the one who was not very much larger than the bunny himself, spied Christopher. He began crawling toward the bunny, holding out some crumbs on one small pink hand.

"Look!" said the bigger people softly. And they sat very, very still.

Slowly Christopher, with his whiskers twitching, crept toward the smallest of the people. Then Christopher Bunny put his tickly-whiskered nose down onto that small pink palm and licked up every sticky crumb.

The crumbs were delicious. Christopher sniffed around happily for more. One of the middle-sized people very quietly held out a piece of lettuce from a sandwich. Christopher sat for a moment, drumming one hind foot thoughtfully. Then he hopped forward and nibbled every bit of that lettuce leaf.

Soon another lettuce leaf appeared, and then a whole delicious raw carrot.

As Christopher Bunny was nibbling the last of the carrot, he thought of Michael and Bridget back in the bramble patch. So with a shake of his round white cotton-puff tail he turned and bounced *lippity clippity* back into the woods.

Michael and Bridget were still asleep in the shade of the bramble patch when Christopher Bunny returned.

"Come on!" he called. "I have a surprise. It's the best exploring I've ever done."

Michael and Bridget woke up with a start. They were hungrier than ever, so off they all hopped, *lippity clippity*, through the woods to the brook.

When they got there, what do you think they saw? Nothing but paper sacks and sandwich wrappers and bare mud along the brook beside the bubbling spring. The people had finished their lunch and gone. And before they left they had picked all the crisp green watercress. Not a bit was left.

"Well," said Bridget Bunny with a toss of her whiskers. "This is a fine surprise."

"Humph," said Michael Bunny. "Next time we'll do our own exploring."

Christopher Bunny patted his round, full tummy contentedly.

"That would be a good idea," he said. And, smiling to himself, off he hopped, *clippity lippity clip*.

The Cock-a-Doodle Train

BEHIND THE SMALL STONE HOUSE where the people lived was a neat vegetable garden. Behind the garden was a wooden tool shed. Beside the tool shed stood the hen house, with a door opening out onto the scratching yard. There, along with Cock Rooster and the other chickens, lived Mrs. Red Hen.

Every day in the chill before the dawn, Cock Rooster strutted out into the scratching yard. Then, as the first pink light of day painted the clouds low in the eastern sky, he hopped and jumped and fluttered up onto the rooftree of the hen house and sang out a mighty "Cock-a-Doodle Doo!"

At this signal, each of the hens in the hen house was expected to lay an egg in the warm straw. Most mornings they all did.

Soon afterward, the little girl who lived in the stone house came into the hen house with a basket on her arm. She spoke softly to the chickens, who fussed and clucked and

fidgeted. Then she reached into the warm straw and plucked out every one of those fresh eggs. She placed them gently in the basket on her arm.

"Thank you," she said to the chickens.

Closing the big door of the chicken house behind her, she carried the fresh eggs into the stone house.

Soon the waiting hens heard another sound. It was the woman from the stone house, calling to let them know that she was scattering handfuls of grain in their scratching yard. The hens, still fussing and clucking and fidgeting, hopped down and out through the small swinging door into the scratching yard. There they enjoyed a delicious meal of tasty bugs and crisp grain.

It was a good life, Mrs. Red Hen had to admit, but now she wanted a change. She wanted to make herself a nest and keep her eggs safe and warm in it until they hatched

14

into baby chicks. She spoke to Cock Rooster about her dream.

"Nests are old-fashioned," said Cock Rooster with a toss of his red wattle. "The people put some of the eggs into the brooder to incubate. It's kept at just the proper temperature, and the baby chicks are cared for very scientifically. That's the way it's done today."

"I don't care," said Mrs. Red Hen. "I want a nice warm nest of my own. I want to watch my very own eggs hatch into baby chicks."

"You'll have to leave the hen house then," said Cock Rooster sternly. But he looked at Mrs. Red Hen with a special sparkle in his bright beady eyes. "I'll help you," he said.

That night when all the other hens were asleep, Cock Rooster lifted some wires of the fence around the scratching yard in his strong beak. And he helped Mrs. Red Hen squeeze under the fence—though she did lose a few feathers on the way.

From outside, Mrs. Red Hen looked back wistfully at her old home.

"Where shall I go now?" she asked Cock Rooster. And she shivered in the night air.

"You must find a place that's sheltered and warm," Cock Rooster told her, "and safe from night hunters like Sly-Face the Fox. I wish I could come with you to help you search, but I can't leave my job here." Cock Rooster tried to look disappointed, but he could not completely hide his pride.

"Well, thank you anyway," said Mrs. Red Hen. Then she fluffed up her feathers and started off *pick-peck* down the gravel path that led toward the people's house.

Red Hen's first thought was to make her nest under the berry bushes at the back of the people's garden. But as she drew near, Barker the Dog woke up and began to howl.

Mrs. Red Hen was not really afraid of Barker, but she didn't want him nosing around her nest with his big red tongue lolling hungrily. She could not make her nest near the house, she decided, because of Barker the Dog.

That was a disappointment, but Mrs. Red Hen was not discouraged. She turned her back on the house and garden and made her way *pick-peck* across the meadow, looking for a safe, warm spot.

The rustling of the tall grass on the meadow made her uneasy. She heard the low hoot of Hunter Owl. She saw his dark shadow slide across a pale cloud overhead. Mrs. Red Hen stood so still that she didn't even breathe until that shadow vanished from sight. She knew now that the open meadow was not the place for her nest, because of Hunter Owl.

At the far side of the meadow, Mrs. Red Hen came upon the bramble patch. Its thick branches dipped down to the ground.

"This would be safe," thought Mrs. Red Hen. "And it should be warm inside."

So she scrunched herself down and pushed in under the wall of brambles. Inside she found a nice warm nest, with layers of soft dust and cozy leaf beds.

"A ready-made nest," thought Mrs. Hen happily. "This is just right for me."

But as she was settling down in the cozy nest, fluffing her feathers and thinking about laying her first egg in her new home, she heard a rustling in the brambles.

"There's someone here," whispered a soft voice.

It was one of the rabbit family, arriving home from a moonlight dance on the meadow.

"It's a hen!" gasped another voice.

"Sorry," said a third voice. (It was Christopher Bunny.) "This is our home, and I'm

15

afraid we fill it up and have no room to spare."

"Oh, dear," clucked poor Mrs. Red Hen. "I'm sorry, too." She stepped out of the nest and shook the nice soft dust from her feathers. Then, with Christopher Bunny leading the way, she followed an easier path out of the bramble patch.

"I wish I could help you find a home," said Christopher Bunny. He shivered a little in the cool breeze that swept across the meadow just before the dawn. "All I can say is, don't go into the woods. That's where Sly-Face the Fox lives. It is no place for a red hen."

"Well, thank you anyway," said Mrs. Red Hen. Then she fluffed up her feathers and started off *pick-peck* along the edge of the meadow toward the stream.

Not far beyond the bramble patch, a bridge crossed the stream. Over the bridge ran a railway track. It was a small railway as railways go, and the train that ran on it was a small train.

Every morning at dawn the train set out from the town to chug across fields and meadows and through the woods to the city some miles away.

This particular morning the engineer stopped the train near the bridge. Then he hopped down from the locomotive cab to fill his coffeepot with water from the stream.

As the engineer was filling his coffeepot, along the bank of the stream came Mrs. Red Hen. She was tired now. She had come a long way. She walked very slowly, *pi-ck-e-ty pe-eck*.

At that moment, down the other bank came Sly-Face the Fox on his way home from a night's hunt. It had been a poor night for Sly-Face. He had not a bite to take home to his hungry family. His proud tail,

16

which usually waved like a plume, dragged low in the meadow grass. Then he spied Mrs. Red Hen.

Fortunately, Mrs. Red Hen saw Sly-Face at the same time. Her heart began to thump. What could she do? Looking swiftly around, she saw the big black shape of the locomotive up ahead. She could feel its warmth, and she could hear its breath—or so she thought—puffing softly, *chuff, chuff, chuff*. She did not know what it was, but it sounded peaceful and friendly. It looked big and strong. It looked as though it would be nice and warm.

Just as the engineer was climbing back into his cab in the locomotive with his coffeepot, Sly-Face the Fox made a leap toward Mrs. Red Hen. Mrs. Hen fluffed her feathers and flapped her wings and fluttered up toward the big black locomotive. She found a resting place just in front of the cab, beside the warm boiler.

The engineer had left a big soft rag there, a rag he used for polishing the boiler. Mrs. Hen settled down on it.

"How lovely," clucked Mrs. Red Hen to herself. "A ready-made nest for me!" And she snuggled into its folds, safe and warm.

Chuff, chuff, CHUFF! The locomotive started off with a tremendous noise. Mrs. Hen was frightened, but she did not know what to do. So she tucked her head under one wing and stayed where she was.

Soon she became accustomed to the noise. She rather liked the swaying motion of the locomotive as it chugged across the meadow. Just as it passed behind the hen house, the first pink light splashed across the clouds low in the eastern sky.

From across the meadow Mrs. Red Hen heard a familiar sound. It was a mighty "Cock-a-Doodle Doo!" Cock Rooster was strutting on the rooftree of the hen house, welcoming the day.

At this familiar signal, Mrs. Red Hen took a deep breath and laid an egg in her new nest. Then she felt really at home.

When the train reached the station in the big town, the engineer hopped down from his cab and reached for his soft polishing cloth. It was then that he found Mrs. Red Hen on her nest, clucking over an egg.

Now, the engineer was a warmhearted man, so he hurried into town and bought some grain. He also got himself a new polishing cloth. Then he found two bowls, one for grain, the other for water. He placed them very carefully near the nest.

Mrs. Red Hen soon learned when and where it was safe for her to hop down from her nest for a little stroll. All the train crew made friends with her, and before the engineer hopped aboard and the train man waved his flag for the train to start, they made certain that Mrs. Red Hen was safe and comfortable on her nest.

17

Every morning at first light the train chuffed across the meadow. And each morning at Cock Rooster's "Cock-a-Doodle" to welcome the day, Mrs. Red Hen laid another egg, until her cozy nest was full of as many eggs as she could comfortably keep warm.

Then she settled down to wait, day after day after day.

At last one morning Mrs. Hen began to feel the eggs quiver under her. Small beaks inside them began to *peck-peck-peck* at the shells.

Soon the shells cracked open, and out tumbled small baby chicks. Their down feathers were damp at first, but as the train moved along the warm breeze soon fluffed them out into soft balls. And the chicks learned to peck, along with their mother, at the bowl of grain.

Summer was coming on and the days were starting earlier. Cock Rooster was welcoming the dawn before the small train came along.

One day, though, the engineer stopped the train just behind the hen house. The engineer and the train man lifted Mrs. Red Hen and her baby chicks and stood them in a line along the top of the locomotive. Then the train man waved his flag and the engineer blew his whistle until all the people in the small stone house and the other houses nearby came running out to look.

Barker the Dog nearly went wild in the garden, and set all the hens to fluttering and fussing. Cock Rooster hopped to the roof of the hen house to see what was happening. When he saw the little family on top of the locomotive, can you guess what he did? He gave the mightiest "Cock-a-Doodle Doo!" of his whole important life!

Now Cock Rooster greets that train every day as it goes by. Mrs. Red Hen fluffs her feathers at the sound and looks proudly at her little family. And all the people who live in the houses around the meadow smile and say, "There goes the Cock-a-Doodle Train."

Note: There really was a little red hen who not long ago made a nest and hatched her family of baby chicks beside the boiler of a locomotive on a small railway very much like this.

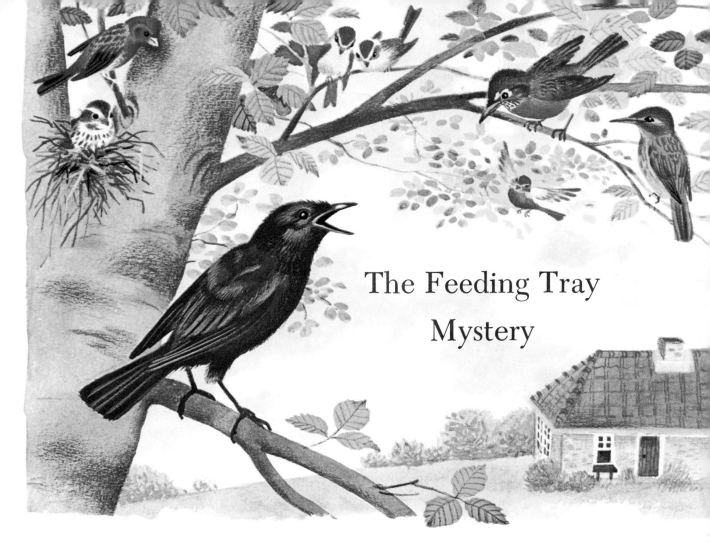

The Feeding Tray Mystery

"NEW PEOPLE in the pink house," Crow reported in his loud voice. The birds living in the big beech tree did not even have to stop what they were doing to listen to him. They could not help hearing anything noisy Crow said.

"Nice big feeding tray at the back window," he cawed. "Good food." He clacked his beak in a satisfied way and went strutting across the lawn.

"If Crow has been there," said Mrs. Robin to her mate, "there is probably nothing left for us."

She gave a hard peck at the stalk of straw she was trying to tuck neatly into her new nest.

"Don't worry about that straw, old girl," said Mr. Robin, sitting back on a branch above the nest to watch her. "Your nests are always nice and snug, and you lay the

prettiest eggs to be found anywhere around."

That was true, Mrs. Robin thought. And her babies were happy and healthy, and very good eaters, too.

Thinking of eating reminded Mrs. Robin of the new feeding tray.

"Let's take a look," she suggested to Mr. Robin. So away they flew, to the branch of a tree not far from the back window of the pink house.

They soon spotted the feeding tray outside the window. A troop of sparrows were just cleaning up the last of the seeds, but as the robins fluttered closer for a look, the window above opened, and one of the people tossed a handful of mixed seed and some bread crumbs onto the tray.

Mr. and Mrs. Robin landed there with a double bounce and speedily pecked up a nice meal.

19

They went regularly to the feeding tray each morning after that. It was a busy place, with sparrows, starlings and finches as regulars. Other birds on the move stopped by as they passed through.

Sometimes the people were a few minutes late opening the window to put out the food. Then the starlings and sparrows—and Jay and Crow if they were around—held a loud and impolite discussion of the people's carelessness until the window opened and a hand appeared to scatter seed.

One morning the people were later than usual. Crow marched crossly up and down the feeding tray making rude remarks. Then he noticed that the window was open a crack. He poked his beak in, hoping to find a seed or two. What he did find was even more interesting. It was a bright gold ring with a shiny stone.

Crow liked bright, shiny things. He had quite a collection of them—buttons, twists of colored foil, pins, even a coin or two—in his messy nest high in the beech tree. This ring would make a nice addition. So with his beak he slid it onto the outer sill where he could pick it up.

He pushed a bit harder than he had intended, and the ring slid onto the feeding

tray, Then, before Crow could snatch it up, the window opened wider and the usual hand scattered seed, hiding the ring from sight.

Crow was soon so busy nibbling seeds that he forgot all about the ring. When he had had his fill, he let other birds come. They pecked and poked this way and that, and in the hubbub the ring was pushed off the tray. It fell into the grass.

It was not until later in the day that the people realized that the ring was gone.

The lady of the house said, "Where is my ring? I am sure I left it on the kitchen windowsill when I washed the breakfast dishes this morning. Now it isn't there."

"It wasn't there when I fed the birds," said the boy of the house. "I would have seen it."

"Are you sure?" his mother asked. "You are certain you didn't accidentally push it off the sill onto the feeding tray?"

"I'm certain, Mama," said the boy.

"Go out and look on the tray and lawn anyway, Son," said the man of the house.

So the boy checked the now empty feeding tray. And he hunted in the grass beneath the tray. But the grass was rather high, and the ring could not be seen.

Days passed, and the lady of the house was more and more upset over the loss of her ring. The birds, of course, didn't know that anything was wrong. They came every morning as usual to eat at the feeding tray.

One night there was a summer shower. In the morning the ground was dotted with fat earthworms that had crawled to the surface. Mr. and Mrs. Robin were delighted. They didn't even go to the tray that morning. Who would eat dry seeds when they could be feasting on fat, fresh worms?

Mrs. Robin found the biggest, longest worm of all. It was still half in the ground, and she pulled and tugged trying to get it out. Mr. Robin came to help her, and together they pulled the worm free. Circled around its middle was the lost ring!

The robins were surprised to see the ring, but they did not share Crow's liking for shiny things. All they wanted was the worm.

Crow, happening by, spotted the bright stone. There was his lost treasure! Down he flew with a great flapping of shiny black wings. He squawked so rudely that he frightened Mrs. Robin half out of her wits.

Mr. Robin had had just about enough of Crow's rudeness. He didn't like having Mrs. Robin frightened, and he was not going to give Crow that marvelous worm! So Mr. Robin ruffled his feathers and spread his wings and stood over the worm with the ring around its middle. He was ready to give Crow a good sharp peck if he came any nearer.

Mrs. Robin was chirping with fright. Crow was cawing saucily. There was such a hubbub that the boy in the house came out to see what it was about. Usually the birds flew away when he came near, but today they were too excited to notice him. As the boy stepped quietly closer and closer, he saw something shining in the wet grass.

"Mama!" he cried. "It's your ring!"

As he bent to pick it up, the birds fluttered away. The worm dangled from the ring, but the boy was not going fishing that day, so he was not interested in earthworms. He let it drop to the grass.

Mr. Robin darted forward and snapped up the worm. With its two ends dangling from his beak, he flew off toward the nest with Mrs. Robin close behind.

Crow was annoyed to see his bright treasure snatched from him. He told the boy what he thought about it, in his crossest terms.

"Crow was trying to tell me something," the boy told his mother as he handed her the ring. "I think he was trying to tell me that he was the detective who found the ring for us."

If Mr. Robin had heard that, and had understood people-talk, he would have chirped, "Detective, humph! Isn't that just like Crow?"

Mr. Beaver Moves to Town

FAR UP THE STREAM that wanders through the big woods, Old Beaver built a dam and family home some years ago. Old Beaver was a sober, hardworking fellow. Life was all cut, haul and scurry for him. Very rarely did any of the woods folk see Old Beaver sit back, leaning on his broad flat tail, and take time to relax, perhaps picking wood chips out of his big orange teeth with a sharp paw nail.

To build his dam across the stream, Old Beaver had to cut down trees and drag the logs to the water's edge. Then, pushing the logs out into the water, he had to tow them to the spot he had chosen for his dam. He filled the spaces between logs with twigs and armloads of mud, until the dam held back enough water to form a nice wide pond in the woods.

In the pond, on the stream side of the dam, Mr. Beaver built his house. For safety, its door was underwater. Inside, a smooth

mud corridor led up to the main living-and-sleeping room. This was a nice, big, comfortable room.

There was plenty of space for beds for the babies. They were soft beds of leaves and grass, with some roots and small twigs mixed in. Old Beaver and his wife preferred to sleep on the smooth mud floor. All around the big room were heaps of twigs and leafy branches. These were the family's food supply.

Old Beaver and his wife had raised several families of young ones in their pleasant home in Beaver Pond. They were well thought of by the neighbors—the deer and squirrels, the chipmunks and woodchucks, the foxes and otters and others who came to drink at the pond that was formed by Beaver Dam.

From time to time Old Beaver enlarged the house or built a new doorway. His children learned his trade by working with him.

When they were almost grown-up, which for a beaver is two years old, they said goodbye to their parents and went off to seek their fortunes and to build new homes. But Old Beaver and his wife were content to stay in their comfortable home for the rest of their days.

Every day Old Beaver paddled out to look over his property and perhaps make some small repairs on the house or dam. He was ambling along the bank of the stream one day, searching for some tender young birch or aspen shoots Mrs. Beaver had asked him to bring home, when he realized that something was wrong. Old Beaver's eyes were not very keen, but he did know People. From what he knew of them, he didn't care much for them. There were people in the deep woods now, whole crews of them, tramping about and peering through eyepieces set up on tall sticks.

Beaver did not understand what they were doing. Actually, they were laying out a road across the big woods, so that other people could build vacation houses along the road.

Though he did not understand the whole project, one part soon became painfully clear. There was a tremendous rumbling in the woods, and a big machine came lumbering along. At the front of the machine, at the end of a long neck, was a mouth with huge teeth. And those huge teeth set to work chewing holes in Beaver Dam!

Soon the water of the pond rushed out through the holes. Only a circle of wet mud among the trees showed where the pretty pond had been. In the midst of the muddy ruin the old beaver's home poked up. Its underground doorway was now high and dry.

"We'll have to move," said Old Beaver sadly to Mrs. Beaver.

And so they did.

23

In the dark of night, while the people were not about, Mr. and Mrs. Beaver swam and paddled down the stream, looking for a place to build a new dam.

Just where the stream flows out of the woods to cross the wide meadow and curve on toward the town, Old Beaver stopped.

He planted his webbed hind feet firmly in the mud of the bank and leaned back on his strong tail for a good look.

"Yes, Mother," said Old Beaver to his wife, "I think this is the place. The stream is not too wide here. There are some good rocks to make a foundation for the dam. And once the dam is built, we will start work on a new home in the pond behind it."

Old Beaver's eyes were not very keen. If they had been, he might have noticed a low building on the far bank of the stream. Even if he had noticed it, he would not have known what it was. As it happened, it was a school for some of the children of the town. Part of the meadow beside the stream was the playground for the children of the school.

Once Old Beaver had decided on the site for his new dam, he wasted no time. For a start he selected a slender willow tree that grew on the bank of the stream. Rearing up on his hind legs, he braced himself on his flat tail and sank his long teeth into the willow bark. He bit out a notch, reached down a few inches and bit out another, then tore out the chunk between the two notches.

Notch, notch, rip, Mr. Beaver slashed his way around that willow, spitting chips of wood on all sides. Soon the willow began to sway and creak. Old Beaver dropped onto all fours and scurried a safe distance away.

Snap! Crash! The willow tree tumbled full length on the bank. In a flash Old Beaver and his wife went to work nipping off the branches. Then they cut the trunk into neat lengths. They nudged the logs into the stream and, tugging and shoving, they towed them out to one of the big rocks. There they laid the logs side by side on the stream bed, facing downstream. Mrs. Beaver packed them tight with mud, while Mr.

Beaver swam back to the shore to cut more trees.

The beavers worked long hours through the warm summer days. *Notch, notch, rip,* they slashed their way around tree after tree. As each tree creaked a warning, the beavers scampered a safe distance away. After each tree toppled with a boom and a crash, back came the busy beavers to nibble it clear of branches and twigs, and to trim it into lengths just right for the dam.

Soon the row of posts stretched across the stream. *Slap, slap, pat,* Mrs. Beaver's busy tail plastered them with pebbles and mud. Higher and higher rose the dam, until only trickles of water wriggled through it to travel on downstream.

Behind the dam the waters spread out to form a nice wide pond. The beaver pond spread out over a part of the meadow. It spread out over the schoolyard. Soon the pond waters lapped at the door of the school itself.

Soon summer was over, and the children of the town were ready to start back to school. But how could they get there? Their school building was an island in the middle of the beavers' new pond!

When the children discovered this, they were delighted. Some of the boys took off their shoes and socks and waded into the pond. Some of the girls dabbled their toes at the edges. They thought it was great fun, but the teachers did not.

The teachers marched down to the Town Hall and told the mayor, "This beaver dam must go!"

The mayor called together the men from the Water Department and the Street Department and the Power Department and the School Department and the Department of Emergency Planning. They all rode down to where the bridge crossed the stream. They stood on the bridge and looked upstream toward the woods. There was Old Beaver himself hard at work at a paper-barked birch tree, *notch, notch, rip.*

"This must stop!" the mayor said.

25

"Right you are!" said the men from the Water Department and the Street Department and the Power Department and the School Department and the Department of Emergency Planning.

"That beaver dam must go!" said the mayor, pounding a fist on the railing of the bridge.

"That it must!" said the men from all those departments, frowning their fiercest frowns.

So they had a hearing and appointed a committee and set to work to analyze the problem. After a couple of weeks they sent a man with a power shovel to chew into the nice new dam.

The water flowed through the dam then, and ran downstream, and the new beaver pond disappeared. In its place there was once again a meadow—rather soggy now—and a schoolyard coated with mud.

As for Mr. and Mrs. Beaver, they were camping out in a temporary burrow dug into the stream bank, since they had not yet had time to build a home out in the new pond. When they heard the rattle and clang of the power shovel, they peered out of their burrow.

Seeing the big teeth of the power shovel tearing into their dam, Mrs. Beaver hissed angrily at it. But Old Beaver just shook his head and mumbled to himself. Then he stroked his chin thoughtfully with one paw and thought his own deep thoughts.

After dusk, when the power shovel had left for the day, the beavers went back to work. They pushed the tumbled logs back into place, bringing fresh armloads of mud to plaster them firmly again. *Slap, slap, tap* went their flat tails all through the night. But no one heard them except Hunter Owl and Sly-Face the Fox as they hunted across the meadow.

The next day was a Sunday, so the power shovel men did not work. The teachers and children did not go to school. Only the beavers went on working. *Notch, notch, tear,* they cut more trees, farther back from the stream this time, where the woods began to thicken. *Push, push, tug,* they got the logs to the stream and then into place to strengthen the dam.

By Monday morning, when school re-opened, the dam was as strong as ever. Old Beaver and his wife were busy patting a fresh coat of mud onto the upstream side,

facing the pond. As for the pond, it spread out as wide and smooth as before. It spread across part of the meadow, over the school grounds, and up the steps of the school itself.

The children were delighted to find their school an island once again in the middle of Beaver Pond. But if the children were pleased, the teachers were not.

The teachers marched again to the Town Hall and told the mayor, "This beaver dam must go!"

The mayor telephoned his department heads. He pounded on his desk as he talked to them. The department heads telephoned one another. They rumpled their hair and moaned.

Then someone called the power shovel man and shouted at him. He took his power shovel and drove *chunk-a-lunk* out to the stream. There he shoveled a great big chunk of logs and mud right out of the middle of Old Beaver's new dam.

Old Beaver in his burrow in the cool mud bank heard the power shovel go *chunk-a-lunk-CRUNCH*. He knew what was happening. He just mumbled to himself and stroked his chin with one paw. But Mrs. Beaver peeked out the doorway of the burrow and hissed as loudly as she could at the power shovel man.

As soon as dusk had fallen and the power shovel man went *chunk-a-lunk* home with his big machine, the two beavers came out and went to work again repairing their battered dam. This time a group of boys from the school were there to help them, lifting small stones and fitting them into weak spots in the dam wall. They were not much help, but the beavers appreciated their spirit.

The teachers did not. Next morning, when the schoolyard was flooded once again, the boys waded out to show their teachers where they had worked on the dam.

The teachers told the mayor, and the mayor tore his hair. Something had to be done—this couldn't go on!

The mayor called in all the department heads and they tore their hair, too, but they did not know what to do. So they all just sat with their heads in their hands.

When it was closing time at Town Hall, the janitor came down the corridor with his sweeping powder and his wide brush broom. He saw the mayor and his friends sitting there looking very glum, so he asked them what the trouble was.

"Hm," said the janitor when he had heard the whole tale. He rubbed one hand over his mouth to hide a smile. "That's one smart beaver. There must be a place for him." He scratched his scalp thoughtfully. "I know!" he said at last.

The mayor and the heads of departments, who had been drawing sad little doodles on their scratch pads, all looked up at once.

"My wife has a brother in the Fish and Game Department," said the janitor. "They are looking for lively beavers to resettle up in the mountains. Beaver dams are needed to keep the soil from washing away when the snow melts and the streams are in flood."

"Call them!" cried the mayor, leaping up to shake the janitor's hand.

So the janitor sat down at the mayor's big desk. He leaned back in the mayor's swivel chair and telephoned his wife's brother in the Fish and Game Department.

Next day a truck drove up to the bridge that crosses the stream not far from the big woods. The man from the Fish and Game Department coaxed Old Beaver into a big crate he carried in the back of the truck.

Mrs. Beaver came too, hissing angrily. But she soon found that the crate was well furnished with bowls of water and stacks of tender leafy twigs and roots and strips of tree bark. So the beavers made themselves at home and quite enjoyed the ride.

By the following day they were high in the mountains. Old Beaver and his wife stepped out of the crate onto a fragrant carpet of pine needles. A lively stream bubbled over rocks between tall pines and sighing cedar trees. Old Beaver planted his webbed hind feet firmly, leaned back on his strong flat tail, and took a look around.

"Yes, Mother," said Old Beaver to his wife, "I think this is the place for us."

So they set to work, *nibble, nibble, notch.* Soon they had a dam in place across the bubbling stream. A nice wide pond spread out behind it, and there, in the shelter of the pond, the beavers built themselves a comfortable lodge.

Old Beaver is still a sober, hardworking fellow. Very seldom does he sit back, leaning on his flat tail, and relax. But once in a while at twilight he does, when the deer and moose, otters and bear come down to the pond to drink. Then they all gather around, and Old Beaver tells the story of the time when he moved to town.

Note: There really was a beaver not long ago who built his dam across a stream and flooded a village school. He really did baffle the grown-up people, and the children did think it was great.

Red Squirrel's Great Nut Hunt

RED SQUIRREL stepped out of his tree-hollow home and sniffed the autumn air. A chilly wind was storming through the treetops high above with a roar like the distant sea. It set even the sturdiest trees to creaking, and sent the last dry leaves rattling down from their twigs.

Red Squirrel was glad of his snug fur coat. "Winter is coming!" he said to himself. "This is what my mother has told me about. I must hurry and find some more nuts."

Away scampered Red Squirrel through the trees, leaping from branch to branch. At the fork of a big oak tree he found Prickly Porcupine munching a strip of bark.

"Winter is coming!" chattered Red Squirrel. "There is no time to waste. We must all hunt for nuts."

Prickly Porcupine blinked his eyes sleepily. He did not really like nuts very well, and the cold weather made him feel like resting. But Red Squirrel was tugging at his quills and made the nut hunt sound so important that Prickly shambled to his feet and followed Red Squirrel down to the ground.

There they met Brown Bear Cub munching on berries.

"Winter is coming!" said Red Squirrel. "There is no time to waste, Brown Bear. Come and help us hunt for nuts."

Brown Bear Cub rubbed his nose with a berry-stained paw. He really liked berries and honey, and fresh fish, much better than nuts. But Red Squirrel was dancing about so excitely that Brown Bear Cub followed along.

Soon Red Squirrel spied Sniffy Skunk peering shyly out from behind a curly fern.

It was easy to recognize Sniffy, even when she hid her face, by the wide white stripe down her black back.

"Winter is coming, Sniffy!" cried Red Squirrel. "There is no time to waste hiding behind curly ferns. Come and help us hunt for nuts."

Sniffy Skunk was not certain what nuts were for, but Red Squirrel was tugging at her ear and it all seemed so important that Sniffy came along.

Under the big old hickory tree Red Squirrel set them all to hunting fallen nuts. They hunted so well, while Red Squirrel ran around chattering excitedly, that soon they had a big stack of hickory nuts.

Red Squirrel stuffed as many nuts into his round cheeks as they would hold. Then he and his friends filled their arms with the rest, and they started for Red Squirrel's hollow-tree home.

"Faster!" cried Red Squirrel, though it was hard for him to speak clearly now, with so many nuts in his mouth. "We must get all these nuts into the hollow tree before the first snowflakes fall."

Prickly Porcupine and Brown Bear Cub and Sniffy Skunk really could not understand what Red Squirrel was saying. They could see his fluffy tail waving excitedly, though, as he raced along to show them the way. So they hurried after him as best they could with their loads of nuts.

At the foot of Red Squirrel's tree, they met Mother Porcupine.

"Whatever are you doing with those nuts, Prickly?" she asked.

"Red Squirrel says that winter is coming," said Prickly. "There is no time to waste, he says. So we've all been gathering nuts."

"Humph!" said Mrs. Porcupine, bristling. "Red Squirrel may need nuts for the winter, but we have plenty of tree bark handy. We can munch on it while we sit quietly dozing through the long winter. Let Red Squirrel gather his own nuts. Come along now."

Prickly Porcupine dropped his load of nuts. And without so much as a wave of his quills, he shuffled along after his mother.

No sooner had the porcupines disappeared than there was a great crackling of twigs nearby. Through an opening in the brush Mother Brown Bear's big head appeared.

30

"I've been looking everywhere for you, Cub. Where have you been? And what are you doing with those nuts?" she asked.

"Red Squirrel says winter is coming," said Brown Bear Cub. "He says there's no time to waste, so we've been gathering nuts."

"Ruff!" snorted Mother Bear, cuffing her youngster with a heavy paw. "Let Red Squirrel find his own food for the winter. You and I have our winter's food supply tucked away in our tummies. We'll sleep snug and warm in our cozy cave and let the winter howl outside. But Red Squirrel is right about one thing. There is no time to waste. So come along with me right now."

Brown Bear Cub dropped his load of nuts. With a wave of one paw he padded away after his mother toward the cave she had chosen for their winter sleep.

Sniffy Skunk smelled a familiar fragrance. Mother Skunk was standing close by, slowly waving her plumed tail, as she did when she was annoyed.

"I've been looking everywhere for you, Sniffy. Where have you been? And what are you doing with those nuts?" she asked.

"Red Squirrel says winter is coming," said Sniffy with a sleepy yawn. "He says there is no time to waste, so we've all been gathering nuts."

"Winter is coming, true enough," sniffed Mrs. Skunk. "But we don't need any nuts to see us through. We'll be safe in our burrow, curled into warm balls, before the first snowflake falls in the woods if you'll come along with me."

Sniffy dropped her load of nuts on the ground. Blinking her eyes and yawning again, she followed her mother's high-swaying tail down the woodland path.

Red Squirrel watched them go. As he sat there, leaning against his fluffy tail, something cold touched him on the nose. He reached up with a paw. There was nothing there but a small damp spot. Again came the feathery touch of cold. Now Red Squirrel could see against his fur the tiny white star of a snowflake. As he reached for it, the snowflake vanished, but others soon appeared.

"I was right!" said Red Squirrel happily. "Winter is coming! In fact, it is here. And what a nice stock of nuts my friends have helped me gather."

Then up the trunk he scampered to carry the first load of nuts to his tree-hollow home.

Mountains and Valleys

HAVE YOU ever been up in the mountains? Mountains are higher than the tallest hill. Some are steep and rocky, with sharp, snow-tipped peaks poking into the sky. Others are more gently rounded. From above they seem to be carpeted with green, but what looks like a carpet is often really a forest of tall trees. Everything in the mountains is big, it seems.

Lakes in the mountains are mirrors set among the rocks, slate gray when the sky is cloudy overhead, bright blue when the sun shines.

Streams run swiftly down the steep slopes, or wander across gentle valleys that lie between the peaks. In the summer these valleys are pretty places, dotted with thousands of small bright flowers. Grass grows fresh and sweet, enough to feed many hungry animals.

Berries ripen on the bushes. The grasses grow tasty seeds. There are fish in the

streams, and lots of juicy roots to be dug up. Bears, ground squirrels, beavers, rabbits and many other animals make their homes in high, wide valleys and on the wooded slopes.

There are mountain areas where people live, too, and they bring sheep and goats and cattle to enjoy the summer pasture.

Higher still in the mountains, the slopes are rockier. Trees no longer grow. Wild sheep, goats and antelopes that live above the timberline must work hard to find enough small plants to feed on. It is fortunate that they can pick their way skillfully over jagged rocks as they hunt.

It is very cold much of the time in the high mountains. But the animals who live there do not mind the cold. They wear coats of long, thick wool, with very soft, fine undercoats beneath.

Sharp twigs on the mountain bushes tear off some of this soft, fine undercoat as the animals pass by. The few people who live in these high mountains—different mountains in different lands—gather the fleece. They spin it into very fine yarn. It makes the softest, warmest cloth.

There are big wild cats that live in the high mountains, too. Cougars, lynxes, mountain lions and snow leopards can climb very well. They can also leap and land safely on their padded paws. They need these skills as they hunt meat for their food.

Overhead, some of the biggest birds on earth circle and glide above the mountain slopes. There are eagles and condors whose wings spread wider than a big man can reach with his arms. They have sharp eyes to hunt for food among the rocks below, and sharp claws to seize it with.

There is not much food to be found in the highest mountains, whether one eats plants or other animals.

When winter snows pile high in the forests on the lower slopes, some of the animals hide away and sleep until spring. We say they hibernate.

Others, like deer and elk, must paw through the snow in search of a little dry grass to eat. Even if they travel down to lower valleys, winter is a difficult time for them. They are glad indeed when spring comes back to the mountains, bringing fragrant flowers and sweet, delicious new grass.

Kid of the Mountain Explores

KID OF THE MOUNTAIN was tired of staying with the other young mountain goats. The rest of the youngsters seemed content in the summer nursery. It was on a pleasant mountain slope. Low, leafy shrubs grew over many of the rocks. There were plenty of tufts of grass and small flowering plants to nibble. But Kid of the Mountain wanted to do more than eat and sleep. He wanted to explore.

There were always nannies watching over the young kids at play. Many of the nanny goats had babies of their own in the group. Others just helped look after the young. They kept close watch, so it was difficult to get away.

Kid of the Mountain thought he could get along very well by himself. He had been able to stand and to leap in small, stiff-legged jumps from the time he was a half hour old. He had learned to freeze and stand

motionless as a stone when a big eagle swept low over the slope hunting food. He knew how to hide when he caught the odor of a hunting cat in the mountain breeze.

Kid of the Mountain wanted to be like the big father billy goats. They did not stay near the nursery. They wandered far and wide. Kid could often see one of them high above. He would be peering out from some rocky ledge, his white beard waving in the wind.

How Kid longed to see what the big billys saw! From the nursery slope he could catch only small glimpses of the wooded valley far below. But from those high cliffs, surely one could see the whole world!

"Just wait," his mother nanny told him. "Our whole band will be traveling down the slope into the forest soon. We will visit a salt lick there. You'll like that. Salt is so delicious.

"There will be excitement enough, too, traveling through the forest. We must be on guard all the time. Bears and packs of wolves and other hunters live there. Last summer I myself had to stab my horns into a big black bear that was trying to bother the kids."

"I don't want to wait," bleated Kid of the Mountain, kicking up his sharp little hoofs. "I want to have an adventure, and I want it right now!"

Nanny Goat sighed. Her yellow eyes were solemn as she chewed her cud and watched the restless little kid.

Soon another nanny called her to come and taste some delicious, spicy leaves. "Come along!" his mother called to Kid of the Mountain. She started across the slope.

Kid of the Mountain did not follow her. He stood watching until she reached the tasty bush. He waited until he saw her bend her head to nibble. Then away he went, out of sight behind a rock!

Up the slope Kid leaped from rock to rock, as he had seen the big billy goats do. The small suction cups on the soles of his feet kept a firm grip as he landed. Then off he would go again.

"This is the life!" said Kid to himself. A breeze rippled through the thick, fine wool of his fleecy undercoat. Even the breeze felt different and exciting, now that he was on his own.

He was high enough to look down upon the nursery slope. He stopped once, to watch the other little kids at play.

"Silly little kids!" he thought. He felt very grown up and proud. But still he was not where he wanted to be—on the high cliff from which, sitting on their haunches, the big billy goats could peer down at the forest and the whole world far below. So on he went up the rocky slope.

On these rocks the big billy goats walked with care. They set each foot down lightly first, to test the ledge. But not young Kid of the Mountain! He leaped swiftly along a narrow ledge.

Suddenly, around a turn, the ledge ended. Ahead of Kid was a solid wall of rock. There was nowhere for him to go!

Poor Kid of the Mountain! The ledge was so narrow that he did not have room to turn around. Far below him spread the green carpet of the forest covering the valley floor. But Kid of the Mountain could not enjoy the view he had come so far to see. He bleated with unhappiness and fear.

Not far away an old billy goat heard his bleating cry. Carefully the old billy goat picked his way to the cliff edge. From there he could see young Kid of the Mountain, trapped at the end of the narrow ledge.

"Back up!" he called. But young Kid was too frightened to edge backward along the trail.

"Stay very still then," called the old billy goat. "I will come."

Kid of the Mountain remembered his mother's training when he had been very young. He froze and stood as still as a stone. It seemed a long, long, lonely time. How he wished he were back on the nursery slope, with a kind old nanny goat watching over him and all his little friends.

At last, behind him, he heard the clink of hoofs on stone. Old Billy Goat was picking his way carefully along the narrow ledge.

"Well, youngster," said Old Billy, "you have come a long way by yourself. Now you can see why we have rules for young kids, and nurseries where you should stay."

"Yes," said Kid of the Mountain sadly. He did not even dare to look over his shoulder at Old Billy Goat. If he could not turn here, how could that big old billy goat?

"There is only one safe way for us to get out," said Old Billy. "You must do just as I say."

"I will," promised Kid.

"Turn slowly toward the cliff," said Old Billy. "I know there is not room for you to turn around on all fours. You must plant your front feet up on the cliff wall and lean your weight on them."

Slowly, slowly, Kid of the Mountain turned his face toward the cliff. He lifted one shaky forefoot as high as he could. He leaned on it until the little suction cups on the sole of his foot gripped the stone. Then up went the other foot, even higher on the wall.

Kid of the Mountain was standing straight up on his hind feet, leaning against the cliff. But what could he do now?

"Now turn slowly toward me," said Old Billy.

Kid of the Mountain leaned as hard as he could on one hoof and inched the other hoof along the wall. Soon he could look over his shoulder and see Old Billy Goat nodding his bearded head. He looked very strong and kind.

"Now set your feet down on this side," said Old Billy.

Slowly, carefully, Kid of the Mountain did as he was told. Soon he was standing on all four feet, facing back the way he had come. He could walk back to safety now. But what about Old Billy Goat?

Old Billy himself did not seem certain as to just what he should do. For a long moment he stood with his feet planted far apart. Then, feeling his way, he began to inch backward along the narrow ledge.

Once, his hoof rested on a loose stone at the edge of the path. The stone went rattling over the edge and disappeared from sight.

Old Billy drew back his hoof. Again, for a long moment, he stood perfectly still. Kid of the Mountain froze too, and shut his eyes tight.

Then back, back, back Old Billy stepped, one careful hoof at a time. At last he reached a wider spot on the ledge.

"Wait a minute now," he told young Kid.

Carefully the big goat did just what he had instructed the young kid to do earlier. He stood up tall against the cliff wall. Leaning on his front hoofs, he slowly turned around until he too was facing back the way they had come.

Kid of the Mountain let out the breath he had been holding in a happy bleat.

"Now follow me, youngster," Old Billy called back over his shoulder. "And no wandering!"

Kid of the Mountain was glad to have the slow, careful old billy goat to follow. For the sun soon set behind the peak in the west. And a low cloud wrapped the mountain in gray fog before they reached the nursery slope.

There the nanny goats bleated a warm welcome to the little wanderer. Soon he was snuggling against his mother's warm, thick wool.

"I think he's learned his lesson," he heard Old Billy say.

And Kid of the Mountain had.

The Cowbell Alarm

ONE SUNNY MORNING in June, the sound of distant bells awoke the mice. The young mice cocked their ears for a moment, then curled up again in their warm beds. They were sleepy, because they had been dancing by moonlight late the night before. The bells had nothing to do with them, they told themselves.

But a few mice—those who were old enough to remember back as far as a year ago—did not go back to sleep. They sat up and rubbed the sleep from their eyes with small gray paws. Then they hurried to the mousehole doorways of their homes and anxiously peered out.

The big room of the mountain cabin beyond the mouseholes was as quiet as usual. Patterns of sunlight from the high windows lay in squares on the wide planks of the floor. Small rolls of dust moved gently in the sunlight, stirred by fresh air that crept in under the closed front door. The lacy strands of a spider web swayed like a curtain in one corner of the room. On the floor below the web lay a pile of seeds the mice had stored. Yes, all was well.

The old mice listened intently. They could hear the creaking of branches in the old pine trees outside the windows. There was the familiar scrape of twigs against the windowpanes. A floor board creaked. Some birds were quarreling in sharp tones somewhere outside. That was all.

Then came the tinkling of bells again—closer this time. The old mice knew what it meant. The People were coming back up the mountain for the summer. They were bringing their cows up to nibble the new green grass of the mountain pastures.

The cows would stay outside, of course. They would not bother the mice. But the people would take over the cabin where the mice had lived so happily, and the old mice knew what *that* meant!

The old mice scurried back into their mouseholes and woke the youngsters.

"The people are coming!" they squeaked.

"Who cares about people?" mumbled some of the young mice. And they covered their ears and tried to go back to sleep.

"You had better learn to care," said the old mice. They shook the sleepy youngsters by the shoulders to rouse them. "You will not live long if you don't."

39

That woke the youngsters. They followed the old mice out of the mouseholes. Across the floor with a clicking of many small toes they went. And they squeezed under the big front door. Lined up on the split-log doorsill of the cabin, they peered down the mountain path.

The tinkle of bells was louder now. Mingled with the tinkling was a louder jangling tone. The mice did not know it, but that was the sound of the big bell worn by the leader of the herd.

The leader was a wise old brown and white cow. Today she wore a wreath of wild flowers over her horns—blossoms of blue and pink, yellow and white, their long stems braided together by the fingers of the cowmaids.

The girls were walking beside the cows, laughing and talking together. Their striped skirts billowed and swung as they walked. And the cowmaids' laughter tinkled as bright as the sound of bells. The young mice were fascinated by the size of these people—the first they had ever seen.

The old mice found the people interesting, too, but they were ready to run.

A faint path led up from the mountain trail, through the pines to the cabin door. At the start of this path two of the girls waved and called their goodbyes to the others. Then they turned toward the cabin.

"Come!" squeaked the old mice. "It's time to go. Back to the mouseholes, everyone!"

Some of the young mice dutifully scampered under the door, across the floor and into the mouseholes. But a few could not see any reason to mind their elders when they were having such a good time.

"Why?" they whined. Or, "In a minute. We're coming."

When the girls were so close that the mice could see the color of the soles of their shoes when they lifted their big feet to take a step, the rest of the young mice scam-

pered away. Only one bold young fellow down at the end of the doorsill did not make it inside.

"A mouse!" cried one of the girls when she saw him. She picked up a fallen pine twig and swept him right off the sill. He tumbled into a heap of soft pine needles with some small seeds mixed in. For the moment he enjoyed the adventure, but it took him a long time to find his way home.

Two other young mice were just nosing into their mouseholes when the girls unbolted and opened the cabin door.

"Look!" said one. "There's a mouse tail just disappearing into that hole!"

"And another over there!" said the second girl. "We'll have to plug those holes."

"And clean up this room!" said the first.

The girls set down their carpetbags full of extra clothes and their sacks full of food on the wooden table. Then they went to work.

With big brush brooms they swept down every cobweb. The spiders saw them com-ing and ran on their long legs to hide behind the rafters. Replacing those cobwebs cost the spiders a lot of extra work, and lost them several tasty fly dinners in the meantime.

The girls also swept the dusty floor. Out the door went the mouse folk's piles of seeds, along with the dust and dirt.

Then the girls filled buckets with water from the spring near the cabin. They washed the dusty windows. Down on their knees they scrubbed the floor until every wide plank shone. They polished the tables and benches, the cupboard and the low stools that stood before the fireplace. They carried the corn-husk mattresses from the bunk beds against the wall out into the sun to air. Some of the stuffing dribbled out through holes the mice had nibbled to get at the dry corn husks.

"Those naughty mice!" said the girls. And with needle and thread and stout cloth they patched every hole.

By the time the afternoon sun dipped behind the mountains in the west, the cabin was shining clean. There wasn't a mouse to be seen in the room.

When one saucy youngster, against his mother's orders, crept to the mousehole to peek out, he found it stuffed tightly with a wad of paper. He tried to push the paper with his nose. It would not move. He tried to pull it with his teeth. It would not come.

"Wait," said the older mice. "When it's all quiet at night we'll go to work on this."

Soon the chilly night air began to seep into the little mouse houses. Nighttime quiet settled over the cabin. Then the mice all gathered at their blocked mouseholes.

Some nibbled at the papers the girls had wadded there. Some tugged with their teeth and tore off bits. Others leaned their shoulders against the paper wads and pushed. At last they felt the papers begin to move. Slowly the wads rolled out onto the floor, sending some mice tumbling after them.

The mice quickly scrambled to their feet. They looked around, their bright eyes astonished. They sniffed the air with whiskers that quivered. How strange the place smelled! Gone was the nice old moldy winter smell of ripe seeds and rotting grass and moist dirt. The cabin smelled of soap and water and sunshine! The old mice's noses wrinkled in distaste.

"Ugh! What's that smell?" squeaked one of the young mice.

"Shh!" whispered his parents. "Don't wake the people or we'll all be in trouble."

"I don't like this," whimpered one of the youngsters. "I don't like having the people here. I don't want to be swept off the doorstep. I don't like having our seeds taken away. I don't like having to tiptoe around and be quiet at night when we used to dance and play. Let's move away."

"Wait," said the parents. "Come quietly. Keep your eyes wide and follow us."

The young mice felt so uneasy that they did just as they were told. They followed their parents so quietly that their small toes scarcely made a click as they crossed the wide cabin floor. They streaked up onto a bench, and from the bench to the tabletop, like silent gray shadows.

And on the tabletop, what delicious smells they found!

"Wow!" One of the young mice could not hold back a squeak of delight.

"Shh!" warned the others. But it was true, the tabletop did smell delightfully of bread and cheese and apple jelly and other good things. And the crumbs the mice found lying about tasted as good as they smelled.

"Look here!" called one bold young mouse. He had found an opening under the cupboard door. It was just large enough for him to squeeze through. "Why bother with crumbs?" he called back. "There's tons of food in here."

He vanished from sight, and the rest could hear a rustling and tearing sound as the bold little mouse tore at paper packages and stuffed himself with the food inside.

"Dangerous! Very dangerous!" worried the old mice, as other young ones followed the first. "It's better to be content with the crumbs."

But some of the young mice were not listening. In the dark cupboard they were having a feast.

When they had eaten their fill, the young mice turned to go. But they couldn't squeeze under the door! Their tummies were too full of food. Now the young mice squeaked loudly for help.

It was too late.

The first rays of the morning sun were creeping through the pine branches outside the cabin window. As the sunlight touched the eyelids of the girls, they awoke.

Hearing the people moving about, the mice scampered down from table and bench and ran for their mouseholes—all but the bold little mice who were trapped in the cupboard.

When the girls had washed and dressed and were ready for breakfast, they opened the cupboard. There they found the torn food sacks. They pulled out the sacks and,

crouching behind them, they found the naughty little mice.

"Oh, those mice!" cried the girls. With stiff pieces of paper they swept the frightened little mice off the shelf onto the floor. Some landed on their backs, with their tiny feet flailing in the air. Before they could right themselves and run, one of the girls

snatched up a broom and swept them out the door.

The little mice lay on the carpet of pine needles for a long moment to catch their breath. Then they scampered into the nearest patch of shade, wishing sadly that they were safe at home.

The rest of the young mice soon learned their lesson. When the cabin was dark and quiet at night, they would follow their parents carefully across the wide floor. Sometimes they found a few crumbs in the cracks between the planks of the floor itself. They found more on the benches and tabletop. But they did not try to squeeze into the cupboard where the people kept their food.

"I'd so like to dance in the moonlight," some of them complained once in a while. Or, "I'd like a good game of hide and seek."

"I don't like having to be careful and quiet all the time," they often muttered.

"But think of the delicious crumbs," their parents said.

And the young mice did have to admit that never had they had so much good food.

So the summer passed.

One morning the mice were awakened by the sound of tinkling bells. But they were not just the bells of the brown and white cows who had spent the whole summer on the sunny mountain slope near the cabin. This was a whole chorus of bells, with one jangling louder than all the rest.

Closer and closer came the bells.

"Are more people coming?" the young mice asked.

"The people are leaving," said the old mice, with wise nods of their heads. "The summer is ending."

Late that afternoon all the mice gathered once more on the cabin doorsill. They watched the two girls, with their carpetbags and empty food sacks, join the others who

44

were herding the brown and white cows. Laughing and talking, they all made their way down the mountain path.

"Are they really gone?" asked the young mice.

"Yes," said the parents.

"Whee!" squealed the youngsters. "We can dance all night. We can play hide and seek again, all over the wide floor."

"They left the cupboard door open, too!" cried one bold young mouse. And he scrambled up, as fast as he could go, into the treasure house.

In a moment he was back at the open doorway, his whiskers drooping sadly.

"There's nothing here," he cried.

Other mice followed him. They poked into every corner of that dark cupboard that still smelled so marvelous. But not a loaf of bread nor a chunk of cheese, not a sack of flour nor a jar of jam—not a bit of food could they find.

The older mice were nibbling the last crumbs from the floor and table.

"The feast is over," they said.

"Oh, no!" wailed the young mice. "How will we get along without bread and cheese?"

"We'll have to work hard again, hunting outside for seeds," said the parents. "But don't forget, when we had plenty of people food to eat, we couldn't dance and play as we wished. Now, even though we must scramble to find our own food, at least the cabin will be ours for the long months ahead. We can line our beds with warm bits from the mattresses for the cold winter. We can stack up our seeds in the corners, and no one will sweep them out."

"And I," said the spider, swinging down from a rafter on his thread of silk, "I can build a web as big as I please, and fill it full of tasty, foolish flies!"

Little Lost Lamb

GRAY Lamb lifted his nose from the thin, tough mountain grass he was nibbling. The breeze that curled down the mountain canyon had a strange sharpness that he did not understand.

Gray Lamb had never known a winter. He did not recognize the smell of coming snow. His mother would have known. She would have nudged him closer to the flock. But Gray Lamb's mother was not there to tell him to hurry. She could not nudge him in the right direction. A hungry wolf circling the flock in the night had caught her.

Gray Lamb did not like the strange feel of the air. He bleated as loud as he could, but the wind tore the small sound to shreds. Anyway, there was no one to hear. Gray Lamb was alone on the rocky mountain slope.

Clouds rolled together across the blue sky above the peaks, shutting out the thin sunshine. The cold grayness made Gray Lamb uneasy. He began to scamper over the rocks, his small hoofs clicking as he ran.

He baaed and baaed again, cocking his small ears to listen for a reply. But the shepherds and their dogs were hurrying the rest of the flock down the trail to the lower pasture, where the sheepfold waited. They were too far away to hear Gray Lamb's calls.

Oh, well, he thought, there was still some dry grass among the rocks. It was not as tasty as it had been when it was fresh and green, but it helped satisfy Gray Lamb's hunger. And it gave him something to do.

He moved along, tearing up and munching the brown stalks until soft white snowflakes began to blow past his nose. Gray Lamb lifted his head to watch them. He put out his tongue and caught some. They tasted cold and wet.

Gray Lamb did not feel cold himself. The soft fluff of the undercoat beneath his blanket of long, curly wool kept him warm. But as more and more snowflakes whirled faster and faster, they blotted out the daylight. All the world was white and gray.

The brown grass at Gray Lamb's feet vanished from sight. Worse still, the rocks vanished, so that he could not tell where to put his feet. He set one hoof on the sharp edge of a rock beneath the snow and stumbled. A sharp little bleat of a cry burst from him.

In a den nearby, Lone Wolf heard that cry. He blinked his yellow eyes and stretched out his big paws. He rose to his feet, flexing his shoulder muscles under his ruff of pale fur. He put his nose out of the den into the whirling whiteness of the snow, then drew it back.

Lone Wolf was not very hungry. He'd already had a big meal of sheep. He wasn't hungry enough to go hunting in that blizzard. If he had had a wife and youngsters to feed, like most wolves, he might have gone. But he had lost his mate. His children were grown. He had left the pack. He was Lone Wolf. He could do as he pleased. So he curled up again in the circle of his own warmth and closed his yellow eyes.

Gray Lamb, lost in white clouds of snow, smelled the wolf. His small heart pounded, for he knew that smell meant danger. Setting his small hoofs down as carefully as he could, he inched away from the smell through the deepening snow.

At last Gray Lamb reached the shelter of a rocky cliff. At its base was a small hollow, protected from the snow. All around, the thick blanket of white heaped up, layer on layer. But against the rock wall there was a small clear space. There Gray Lamb curled up, huddled against the unfeeling rock. He tucked his nose into his thick, warm wool. And there the lonely lamb fell asleep.

When he awoke, the storm was over. A cold wind still whistled down the mountain pass, but now it had blown apart the low, gray snow clouds. Between the clouds, the light from a thin curve of silvery moon glittered on the white world.

46

Gray Lamb lifted his nose, stood up and looked around. All he could see was strange, shining whiteness. This was not the world he knew. He did not know what to do or where to go. So he tucked his nose back into the warmth of his wool and drifted back to sleep.

It was a howl echoing among the rocks that woke him next time. Gray Lamb quivered with fright at the sound. Lone Wolf, he thought. The call came again, but this time it was a sharper, barking sound. Gray Lamb closed his eyes and listened, scarcely breathing. Now there were other sounds as well. And they were coming closer, and closer.

Soon, pushing through the snowbank, a head appeared close to Gray Lamb's own. Gray Lamb could feel a warm breath. Slowly he forced himself to open one eye.

But it was not Lone Wolf who had pushed his way into the small shelter—it was Grandfather Ram! His eyes looked down kindly at the small, frightened gray lamb. With his warm nose and the curve of his curling horns, he nudged the lamb up to its trembling feet and out of the shelter.

Grandfather Ram was not alone. He had come up the mountain with a young shepherd and his dog. They had come to search for any stray sheep who had been lost in the storm. Now together the four started down the slope through the strange white world.

The snow looked soft, but it was covered with a hard crust. The shepherd wore long, slender skis that slipped smoothly over the crust. The sheep dog whose bark had frightened Gray Lamb ran lightly over the snow. Gray Lamb scampered along lightly too, though his small hoofs skidded now and then. Only Grandfather Ram had trouble.

Grandfather Ram was solidly built, with a heavy body under his long, thick wool. His weight made his hoofs crack through the

snow crust. Down he sank, until only his head and curly horns could be seen.

He tried to butt with his horns and push with his heavy shoulders against the white wall that held him. But he could not move.

Gray Lamb was the first to see his trouble. Good Grandfather Ram, who had rescued him! Gray Lamb could not bear to see him suffer.

"Wait!" he bleated to the dog and the shepherd. "Baa! Look! Help!"

In a swooping curve that sent snow flying from the edges of his skis, the young shep-

herd spun around. At his heels came Dog, barking his sympathy for a friend in distress.

Dog ran around and around Grandfather Ram, yipping his advice. But the shepherd knew what to do. He unstrapped his skis and used the point of one to hack through the crust. With his mittened hands he scooped out snow until he had cleared a space in front of Grandfather Ram. With feet and skis he packed the snow hard. Then, tugging good old Grandfather Ram by his curly horns, the shepherd pulled him up the snow slope onto the crust again.

Now Grandfather Ram led the way, with Gray Lamb stepping carefully close behind. Next came the young shepherd, more slowly now, but on his skis again. At the end of the line, Dog raced from side to side, barking impatiently.

Grandfather Ram picked his way with care, testing the weight of the crust before each step. He did not want to break through again!

They made their way slowly. Before they had gone very far, Gray Lamb felt cold, white snowflakes on his nose. Looking around, he saw them dancing in the air.

Soon snow covered Grandfather Ram's thick wool. It clung to Dog's head and lay in a wide white stripe along his back. It whitened the shepherd's cap and shoulders. Gray Lamb could feel its weight on his own back, too.

As the little procession plodded through the whirling whiteness, melting flakes froze to ice around their faces. The shepherd called them to him one by one and scraped away the ice. But as soon as they started on, it formed again; their warm breath melted the snow, and the moisture quickly froze.

Gray Lamb did not like the ice around his nose. He did not like the weight of the snow on his back. He did not like the slow pace, following careful old Grandfather Ram. But he was glad he was not alone!

He was gladder still when he smelled Lone Wolf. Wolf, out hunting again, sniffed

the scent of the sheep. But he also smelled Dog, and the man-smell of the shepherd. There were too many for him to tackle alone. So Lone Wolf retreated to his den.

Plod, plod, plod. Gray Lamb could scarcely keep his legs moving and his sleepy eyes open enough to follow Grandfather Ram's snowy trail. Then suddenly he heard the young shepherd shout, "Hello!"

Gray Lamb peered around the bulk of Grandfather Ram. Through the curtain of thinning snowflakes he saw a small golden glow. He heard the baaing of many sheep.

Dog gave a great, joyful bark. Even Grandfather Ram quickened his careful steps. Soon the dark shape of the shepherds' van appeared ahead. Beside it was the long

low line of the sheepfold where Gray Lamb had been born back in the early spring.

The glow of light from the window of the shepherds' van grew brighter. The door opened and light poured out in a golden pathway across the snow. The dark shape of an old shepherd stood for a moment in the doorway. Then he came hobbling down the steps to meet them.

The gate of the sheepfold opened, and Gray Lamb followed Grandfather Ram inside. The warmth and welcome of the baaing flock surrounded them. The storm, the wind, the wolf, the danger of the cracking snow crust—all were behind them. Grandfather Ram and Gray Lamb were safe at home at last.

Arctic
and
Antarctic

Have you ever thought, "Oh, I wish this day didn't have to end!" To have that wish come true, you would have to travel to the far north or the far, far south—near the North Pole or the South Pole.

There, during the short weeks of summer, there is a "day" that lasts six weeks! The sun never sets, or it dips only for a short time beneath the horizon and then swings

upward again. The wide sky is always light.

In the far north, summer comes in June and lasts through early July. In the far south, summer, such as it is, comes in December and early January.

The continent of Antarctica around the South Pole never really warms up, though. It is almost entirely covered with ice all year. About the only creatures that manage to live on land there are the penguins, those strange birds that walk instead of fly.

The icy seas, with their towering blue-green icebergs, are home to giant seals and huge whales. Wide-winged albatross float across the skies above, and other fish-eating birds swoop down to catch their dinner from the icy waves. There are even birds—terns, for example—that fly every year the thousands of miles from the Arctic to Antarctica and back again. They spend the short summer at each end of the world.

The Arctic, the region around the North Pole, is somewhat warmer than the Antarctic. During the short weeks of summer, small flowers bloom swiftly—red, blue and gold—along the many arctic lakes and streams and on the boggy marshes. Then many birds, especially water birds like geese and terns, and waders like the plovers, fly northward to lay their eggs and raise their families.

There are year-round dwellers in the Arctic, too. Not many humans live there, but there are a few towns and small fishing villages. Some people like the Lapps of northern Europe, the Eskimos of North America and their cousins of Siberia wander over the Arctic hunting and fishing for food.

To most people, the Arctic does not seem a very cheerful place for much of the year. During the long winter, there is little or no daylight. For about six weeks the sun never rises above the horizon. Only pale light comes from the moon and stars.

Winter does not end when the sun begins to creep a bit higher in the midday sky with each passing week. Ice and snow cover the Arctic until late May. Then with a great roar the ice on lakes and rivers, even on the Arctic Ocean, begins to crack and break up.

Some of these huge ice chunks are blown up on the shores by fierce winds. Some are floated, bouncing and bumping, down the rivers to the ocean. All year around enormous icebergs, mostly underwater, float through the northern seas.

If you fly over the Arctic, as many birds do, it seems as if no animals live in this wide and lonely land. If you travel by boat down its rivers in the summer, though, you will be almost certain to meet some of the arctic

dwellers—including hungry flies and mosquitoes!

You may see a large herd of caribou. The flies and mosquitoes are a great bother to them. The caribou, looking like large, clumsy deer, move north in spring from the shelter of the woods. They spend the summer wandering the treeless plain called the tundra. There they feed on grasses, moss and the small bright plants called lichen that grow on many rocks.

Caribou that have learned to live with man are called reindeer. They are somewhat smaller than their wild cousins, with shorter legs and smaller ears.

Wolves may trail the caribou herd, but the arctic foxes are too small to hunt big deer. The foxes feed mainly on birds' eggs, young birds, and the small brown mouselike animals called lemmings.

The largest land animal of the Arctic and near-Arctic is the grizzly bear. The polar bear with its white coat and long neck may be very large, too, but it does not care to spend much time on land. The polar bear lives on the ice, hunting seal, walrus, fish and water birds. It is so well adjusted to icy cold that it does not hibernate during the long dark winters as its cousins farther south do. It hunts all the year around.

Small arctic foxes often follow a polar bear on his hunt. If the bear kills a large animal, they know there will be meat left over for them.

The coat of the arctic fox turns as white as the polar bear's in winter. It may be even whiter, for the polar bear's fur has a yellowish cast. A white coat is good protection in a world of snow. The arctic wolf, the arctic hare, and the ptarmigan, the only bird that winters in the Arctic, all wear white feathers or fur during the long months when their world is white with snow.

A Home for Little Canoe

BABY WHALE gave a small, sad squeak. He could not find his mother. He had always swum close beside her, his nose gently nudging her smooth side. Together they would rise to the surface every few minutes for a breath of air. Then down they would dive, cutting the water smoothly with their sleek bodies. They liked the deep dark waters still cold as ice in the arctic spring.

Baby Whale listened for his mother's voice. How fast he would swim to her if she would only call him softly. But she did not call.

Fish swam close to Baby Whale's nose, but he did not care to catch any. He didn't even feel like playing with them. Sometimes he liked to catch a fish in his wide mouth, then let it go again. But not today.

If his mother had been with him, she would have known that the schools of fish were swimming close to the shore. They were heading for their home river. They would swim up the river and lay their eggs.

Mother Whale would have said, "Take care!" She knew there were dangers close to shore.

Baby Whale didn't know anything about danger. He did not know that on the shore not far away there was a fishing village where People lived. He did not know that the fathers of the village were hunters. They paddled their light skin-covered canoes out onto the icy waters in search of seal or walrus, fish or other food. To them a whale was a treasure.

Baby Whale only knew that he needed air. His mother had been trying to teach him to glide smoothly to the surface. She could coast along so that only the blow hole on the top of her big head and a strip of her smooth back would show above the surface. She did it so beautifully.

53

Baby Whale had not learned the trick. He bounced up so high that his whole wide face and a third of his length rose above the surface.

Up he bobbed, and his wide-spaced eyes peered around him in amazement. That was when he saw the mother whale shape on the surface of the sea not far away. With a happy squeak Baby Whale swam toward the shape. He did not know that it was the human hunters' canoe.

Baby Whale reached the mother whale shape and nudged it with his nose. It was smooth like his mother, with rounded sides. It was warm, and it seemed to move slightly from within. Baby Whale gave a small, low squeak of contentment and snuggled up to the mother shape.

In the canoe, the hunter men watched Baby Whale with surprise.

"This young whale thinks we are its mother," said one with a laugh.

"This will be an easy kill," said another, lifting his pointed spear.

"No," said a third man in a sharp tone. "No, we cannot kill a young one that trusts us. Where there is a baby whale, there will be big ones close by. They are moving northward these days for the summer. We shall hunt a big one. But this baby we must not kill."

"What shall we do with it?" grumbled the man with the spear. He was still holding his weapon firmly in one hand. "A polar bear or a killer whale will not be so kind if they find the baby alone."

"We shall let it follow us if it wishes," said the leader. "Then we shall see. Something will turn up."

At the leader's signal, the men turned their skin canoe toward shore. Soon it was back in the shelter of the small harbor. The men had built this harbor by piling up a

breakwater wall of earth and sod and stones where the shore curved to form a small bay.

Baby Whale followed the boat, still nuzzling its side trustingly.

A little group was waiting on the shore as the men beached their canoe. The children were dancing with excitement. The women were smiling. The hunters looked around to see what was causing the excitement. They soon saw a tall man with light-colored hair and round eyes.

"Ha," said the leader of the hunting party. "Bush pilot. He must bring some news."

The news the bush pilot brought was good. Last winter the villagers had made carvings in stone and walrus tusk. The bush pilot had taken them to town. The carvings had sold for a good price. The pilot had brought back some money and big cartons of food. The whole village could have a big feast, and still save some food for the winter.

"Ha," said the leader of the hunting party. "Then we do not have need of all the fish we have harpooned today. We can give some to feed the small whale."

As the children crowded around, the hunters told the story of the little whale that thought the canoe was its mother.

"What is the whale's name?" a small boy asked.

No one knew.

"The whale must have a name," the children said.

"I know," said a girl whose black eyes danced like shining stones. "Since it thinks the canoe is its mother, let us call it Little Canoe."

When the men unloaded their catch of fish, they gave a fish to each of the children to feed to Little Canoe.

The little whale smelled the good fish smell. He opened his wide mouth in what looked like a smile. And he caught the fish the children tossed to him.

"Can we keep him?" the children asked. "We can go out in our kayaks and catch more fish to feed to Little Canoe."

"We cannot keep him long," said the leader. "It is hard enough to feed ourselves. A whale takes too much food."

"Let me see what I can do," said the bush pilot. "I will fly back to the city tomorrow. I will see if I can find a home for Little Canoe."

When the sun rose next morning over the harbor, Little Canoe looked up at a strange roaring sound overhead. It was the small plane of the bush pilot taking off for the flight to the city. With him he took some pictures the children had drawn of Little Canoe.

Days passed in the small village on the shore. Each morning the sun rose a little earlier than it had the day before. And each day it took a few more fish to satisfy the appetite of that hungry whale Little Canoe.

"We cannot feed him long," the leader admitted, rubbing a hand over his eyes to hide his worry. "He eats too many fish."

"Perhaps Little Canoe would like some birds' eggs," said a small boy. "There are plenty of those on the cliffs."

But Little Canoe did not like birds' eggs.

"Perhaps Little Canoe would like some berries from the marsh," said a small girl.

But Little Canoe did not like berries. He just wanted fish and more fish.

"He takes too many fish," said the man with the spear. "We should kill him." He fingered his hunting knife. "Then we would have some whale blubber and oil, some meat to dry and bones to carve into tools. And we could keep the fish we catch instead of throwing them away to this whale."

"We will wait," said the leader, "until the bush pilot returns."

Day after day passed, and the bush pilot did not come. Rain clouds blew in from the sea and pelted the little village. Waves thundered against the breakwater. The canoes stayed on the beach. There were no fresh fish for the cooking pots, no fish for Little Canoe. He squeaked unhappily.

The man with the spear stroked its point with his thumb. It was good and sharp. "Tomorrow!" he said, and he bobbed his head toward the harbor and Little Canoe.

The children were filled with fear.

In the night the wind changed. It blew the rain clouds out to sea.

Late the next morning, the children heard a familiar roar in the sky. They left the baskets in which they had been gathering birds' eggs and their sealskin sacks half filled with fresh-picked berries. They ran to the flat meadow where the bush pilot liked to land.

The bigger children held the little ones by the hand to keep them out of the plane's way. Soon the plane had landed. The whirling propeller slowed so that they could see the blades. Then out stepped the bush pilot, pulling off his goggles and waving.

"Did you do it?" the children called, dancing up and down. "Did you find a home for Little Canoe?"

The pilot grinned and reached into a pocket of his jacket. He pulled out a folded piece of newspaper.

"Come along," he said to the children. "I will tell everyone at once."

The big children danced at the pilot's heels. The little ones clung to his hands and trouser legs. By the time the bush pilot made his way to the leader's hut, the whole village had gathered there to hear the news.

"I told a friend of mine at the newspaper about Little Canoe," said the pilot. "He printed this story." The pilot showed them the newspaper.

"Baby Whale Needs a Home," it said in big type. Then it told the story of Little Canoe. And there were the pictures the children had drawn of Little Canoe swimming sadly in the bay.

"There's my picture! And mine!" the children cried happily.

"But what about the small whale?" the village leader asked.

"Just yesterday I had a call from a city down south," said the pilot. "This city has a big zoo, a place where wild animals live. The zoo is beside the shore. It has big tanks full of fish. And it has one very big empty tank, filled with water from the sea. It is big enough to be a home for a whale.

"The zoo men will send a boat up for Little Canoe. A big net on a long pole will be attached to it. The net will hold Little Canoe so he will not get lost. He can swim along behind the boat. They will take him to the zoo."

And that is just what they did, those men from the zoo. Today Little Canoe is a grown-up whale. He is one of the most popular of all the animals. Children from miles around come to visit him there.

A newspaper story is posted in a case near Little Canoe's tank. It tells the story of Little Canoe. And it has the pictures the children drew that helped him find a home.

Maybe some day you will visit that zoo and see it all for yourself.

Note: There really was a little whale in the Arctic not many years ago who followed a boat home, thinking it was his mother. He really did find a home in an aquarium, which is a city home for creatures of the sea. And he was named for an Eskimo canoe; his name was Umiak.

Away from the Crowd

VELVET-NOSE LEMMING darted into his home burrow. He was wriggling all over his fat little body with excitement.

"Everybody's moving!" he told his mother. "Let's go too!" He quivered from his velvety nose to the tip of his small white tail. He would have danced, but the tunnel was too narrow for much of a dance.

His mother yawned and curled up more comfortably in her grass-lined bed nook. Babies scampered all around her, squeaking in their high little voices. Mother Lemming was tired from looking after too many babies in the crowded apartment.

"I'm not going anywhere," she said. "For one thing, it's too cold to travel."

She had taken a walk up the twisting maze of burrows to the top of the snow bank not long ago. She had a longing for some fresh grass or a plump, juicy snowberry. But all the grass and moss along the tunnels was dry and trampled.

Near the end of one burrow she had found some berries still clinging to a snow-covered bush, but the berries were frozen hard and dry. Mother Lemming had nibbled a few, because she was hungry, but it was not a very good meal. Then she had wandered on to the top of the tunnel. As soon as she poked her nose out, it was nipped by the cold.

Mother Lemming fluffed up her silky brown fur coat against the cold, but she did not stay at the tunnel doorway long. She was glad to scamper back down the maze of burrows to her own warm nook, where her babies waited. Travel did not appeal to her.

The burrow town was full of excitement, though. She could not help hearing it. Every tunnel was crowded with lemmings running this way and that, calling to one another in their shrill little voices. Now and then two friends stopped to rub noses and have a little conversation. All the talk was of moving.

"The traffic is terrible, my dear. It's hard to get up or down a burrow without bumping into someone."

"Nests are getting so crowded."

"You have to go farther and farther to get food."

"There must be a better way to live."

"We're getting out, as soon as the weather warms up a bit. Why don't you come too?"

Mother Lemming had heard all the talk. She knew that most of her friends were planning to leave. Her young Velvet Nose and his friends were all excited. But Mother Lemming had decided to stay.

When she went out these days, it was to snip off bits of dry grass. She cut them into neat lengths and tucked them into the walls of her round nest. She wanted that nest to shelter her babies and herself until all the snow melted under the summer sun.

As she worked she made a soft chirring sound. It was really a contented little song.

> Home is the best.
> Under the snow,
> Snug is our nest.
> Why should we go
> Out in the cold,
> The sleet and the storm,
> When here below
> We're cozy and warm?

Velvet Nose and the older children did not stop to listen to the quiet little song.

They were bubbling with the excitement that filled the burrow town. They ran around all through the short days, rubbing noses and wrestling playfully with their friends. Wherever they went they heard the excited chattering that echoed up and down the tunnels.

"When do we leave?"

"Maybe tomorrow."

"I can hardly wait."

"It's too crowded here to breathe."

"Everybody's going. It will be wonderful."

Velvet Nose tried to break in to ask a question.

"Where are you going?" he wanted to know.

No one listened to him. He felt excited and upset and confused all at once. So he left the hubbub and made his way to his mother's quiet nest.

Next morning a shrill chattering out in the burrow tunnels awakened Velvet Nose.

"It's the day," he whispered to his mother, poking her gently with his soft nose. "They're all leaving. Can't we go too?"

"No," said his mother. "I'm too sleepy, and there will be too much of a crowd."

"But they're going to get away from the crowd in the burrow," said Velvet Nose.

"Humph," said his mother, tucking her face into her warm fur. "Where are they going? Can they tell you that?"

"I don't know," Velvet Nose admitted. But a great lump of excitement seemed about to burst through his chest. "What does it matter?" he cried, his voice rising. "It's sure to be wonderful."

"Mmmm," came his mother's sleepy murmur as the babies snuggled closer into her fur. "It's wonderful here."

Velvet Nose sighed a deep sigh. He backed out of the nest into the outer tunnel. There he was caught up in a crowd of hustling, bustling lemmings, all chattering at the tops of their voices.

He tried to dig his toes into the smooth floor of the tunnel, but the crowd swept him along with them. Up the slope toward the world outside Velvet Nose was nudged along.

The short March day had ended. The sun had melted the snow crust for a while. But now, with darkness, the cold had crept across the drifts again, freezing their surfaces to a smooth coat of ice.

Across the northern sky shimmered a moving curtain of color—white, gold, blue, green and rose. All the colors of the rainbow glowed against the sky so brilliantly that the stars were dimmed.

Velvet Nose did not stop to admire the sky. The crowd of lemmings was pushing him along. They were leaping, shoving, tumbling over one another.

"This is more of a crowd than there ever was back in the burrow town," Velvet Nose thought to himself. "And no one really knows what they are heading for."

Still, he felt the strong excitement of the crowd. Part of him wanted to go too.

Whack! One of the leaping, shoving young lemmings struck Velvet Nose from behind. He went tumbling under the feet of the hurrying crowd. He was stepped on and punched and pushed this way and that.

59

At last he managed to pull himself out from under the hurrying feet. He reached the shelter of a tuft of willow twigs that pushed up through the snow. There Velvet Nose lay trembling, trying to catch his breath.

After a while he climbed up the willow twigs to see what he could see. All he could see was a carpet of brown furry bodies with sturdy legs kicking out, making the snow fly.

Velvet Nose still felt a longing to be hurrying along with them, but he was too bruised and tired to leap up and run. He lay there, sheltered by the willow twigs, until at last the cold crept through his coat of fluffy fur.

Then, clipping off a bit of willow bark as a gift for his mother, he started for home.

He scarcely recognized the main doorway of the burrow town, the snow had been so trampled by the hurrying crowd. A few late starters were still pushing and shoving in the doorway. He could hear their voices.

"Hurry! Hurry! We must get away from the crowd!" he heard them cry.

Velvet Nose crept on to a deserted back doorway. Wearily he made his way in, down twisting, turning tunnels until he came to a familiar one.

As he drew near his mother's nest, he could hear the small, contented chirping of the babies. All around him was peace and quiet, he realized. Most of the nests were empty. Only now and then from the distance did he hear a small, happy chirr.

"They all left to get away from the crowds," said Velvet Nose to his mother. "Now they're all jammed together out in the cold. The peace and quiet is here."

"I told you so," said his mother, snug in her nest with her babies playing around. She turned to Velvet Nose and gave him a soft nose rub to welcome him back. "I told you home was the best."

Why Leave Home?

LEMMINGS live in burrows they dig into the ground. During the short summer they eat their fill of grasses, willow catkins, moss, leaves and roots. They like to take food home to eat in their own doorways. And they store away big roots in their burrows for the winter.

When snow several feet deep covers their burrows, they dig tunnels through the snow to small bushes and grasses, so they still have food.

Lemmings are about the size of mice, but they eat so much, and have so many families of hungry babies, that they can strip all the plants in their neighborhood bare.

Then the whole burrow decides to move. They keep traveling in a panic, looking for a new home site. If they do not find one, they keep on going, even when they reach a river or the sea. Crowds of lemmings have been seen out at sea on cakes of ice, still hunting for a new home.

Grayling Goose's Big Dinner

ONE MORNING Grayling Goose's mother said, "Tomorrow we leave for the south. Eat your fill today, Grayling, because it will be a long flight and we can't be sure of stopping at very good places to eat."

Grayling felt his heart beat faster. This was the news he had been waiting for.

The brief summer was ending on the far northern lands men call the tundra. The days were growing shorter. Nights were really dark instead of pale gray. Grayling felt the sharp chill in the breeze. It stirred the waters of the marsh, near which his parents had made their summer nest, with cold fingers of air.

All around the marshland birds were gathering in flocks for the long journey southward. There were noisy gulls and terns, long-legged sandpipers, small white snow buntings. And, of course, more of Grayling's uncles and aunts and cousins, the big gray geese, were flying in every day.

Each day the flocks flew off on practice flights. These were not just for the youngsters who had been born in the north that summer and had never migrated. The grown-ups needed to get their flying strength back too.

Grayling especially liked the practice trips. He liked finding his place close behind his mother and father in the long, orderly, V-shaped file. He liked the feeling of growing strength in his wing muscles. Each flight took the geese in a circle larger than that of the day before.

Now Grayling was impatient to leave. He was eager to see the world. Every day it seemed some group or other flew off with a great roar of flapping wings and a squawking or piping of excited voices. As each flight in turn vanished from sight in the cloudy southern sky, Grayling's heart swelled more with excitement.

Now it was to be his turn!

61

seemed that someone was ahead of him, snip-snapping at the food. He began to feel discouraged—and hungrier than ever.

"Hello, Grayling," said a voice near by.

The voice came from the doorway of a house of grass and twigs that rose up in a low mound above the water. In the doorway stood Mike Muskrat, one of Grayling's furry friends.

"What are you looking for?" asked Mike.

"Hello, Mike," said Grayling. "I'm looking for dinner. I have to eat a lot today, because tomorrow we leave for the south."

"I'll miss you," said Mike Muskrat. "It's so quiet and lonely here in the winter. Of all the birds, only the ptarmigans stay. And it's hard to see them against the snow. Have some dinner with me before you go."

And Mike brought out some delicious seeds and grasses and juicy roots from his underwater storeroom.

"Thank you," said Grayling when he had eaten a good meal. "And goodbye. I'll see you again next spring."

Then Grayling swam away with a flip of his wing. Mike Muskrat stood in his doorway, combing his neat fur coat with his paws. He stood watching until his friend was out of sight, hidden by tall reeds.

"Hello, Grayling!" said another voice.

It was Willie Otter, another of Grayling's friends. He was standing on the shore of the marsh, waving one small paw.

"What are you looking for?" Willie asked.

"Hello, Willie," said Grayling. "I am looking for dinner. I have to eat a lot today, because tomorrow we leave for the south."

"Come and play instead," said Willie. "I've built a new mud slide down the bank here, and it's such fun."

He flung himself on his tummy, and down he slid, to land with a splash not far from Grayling Goose.

"Eat your fill today," his mother had said. That was an order Grayling was happy to obey. He was always hungry, it seemed. So he started straight off to look for dinner.

The bog had been full of ripe, red cranberries. The crowberries had been blue and tasty. But with all the flights of hungry birds gathering near the marsh, most of the berries were gone. The heads of the grasses had drooped under the weight of crisp and tasty seeds. But most of those had been snipped off by the sharp teeth or beak of some animal or bird. Tufts of fluffy white still floated up from the cotton grass, but that did not seem like food to Grayling Goose. As for insects, they were beginning to hide away for the winter wrapped in silk cocoons.

Grayling swam and swam among the brown reeds. But wherever he went it

Grayling was not in the mood for the otter's games. With a kick of one webbed foot he turned his back on Willie. Then he began to nip at some last grass seeds that drooped from the muddy bank.

Willie Otter was not discouraged. He dove down into the cold water. Soon he popped up again, in front of Grayling's beak. He held a wriggling fish in his mouth.

Willie's eyes danced with naughty fun as he offered the fish to Grayling. He knew the young goose would not like it. Many birds of the Arctic do eat fish—the terns and gulls, the loons and others—but not the stately gray geese.

Grayling gave a honk of annoyance. So Willie pulled himself up onto the bank and settled down to a fish lunch. He ate swiftly and neatly, from head to tail. The scaly fish tail he tossed aside. Then he wiped his face and whiskers on some dry grass and was ready to play again.

First, though, he pulled up a pawful of roots and tossed them to Grayling Goose.

Grayling did not care for Willie Otter's manners, but he did like those juicy roots. He honked his thanks and ate every bit of the roots. Then Grayling left Willie Otter behind and went on with his hunt.

"Hello, Grayling," a chirpy voice soon greeted him.

On the bank nearby, yawning sleepily, stood Gretchen Ground Squirrel.

"What are you looking for?" Gretchen asked.

"Seeds and reeds and weeds and such," said Grayling. "I am looking for dinner. I have to eat a lot today, because tomorrow we leave for the south."

"Seeds are easy," said Gretchen. "I have a lot on hand. I won't be needing many more, because I'm about ready for my long winter's sleep."

From her burrow near the marsh Gretchen kindly brought out a heap of tasty seeds. She piled them on a floating lily pad for Grayling's lunch.

"Thanks!" said Grayling, tossing them down with one flip of his long neck. "Have a good winter's sleep. I'll see you next spring." And off young Grayling swam.

Soon he came to a clump of birch and willow trees. There were not many trees in the Arctic here. Those that did grow at all were very small.

"Hello, Grayling," said a voice from the small grove. It was Charlie Beaver. He turned away from the sapling he was chewing to smile at Grayling. His smile was full of big orange teeth.

"What are you looking for?" he asked.

"Hello, Charlie," said Grayling. "I am looking for dinner. I have to eat a lot today. Tomorrow we leave for the south."

"Have dinner with me," said Charlie.

Charlie stripped some bark from a birch tree with two tugs of his long teeth. Then he set out a delicious meal of bugs on the clean, peeled wood for Grayling Goose. He himself chewed on a twig.

"I have to lay in some more twigs and branches before winter," Charlie explained.

He waved a paw at his mud and twig house, whose roof poked up above the pond.

"This is really too far north to be good beaver country," he explained. "I should have stayed in the deep woods. There's not enough timber here to keep a family in food. It's hard enough for a beaver alone. I guess I should give up and go back, but I've got this pioneering urge in my blood." He sat back, leaning on his tail, and looked across the wide marsh.

"It's great country to visit," said Grayling between bites. "But from what I've heard, I wouldn't want to live through the winter here."

When he had eaten every beakful he could hold, he said, "Goodbye. Good luck. I'll see you again next spring."

Then on swam Grayling. Soon he was back home at the nest, where his mother was waiting.

The nearby marsh was noisy and full of traffic. Wild geese were flying in and greeting old friends with a good deal of honking and roaring of wings. Grayling's head turned this way and that as he tried to watch all that was going on.

"Oh, Grayling," called his mother, when she spied him. "Come here. I have a delicious dinner of fresh roots and seeds for you. I know how hungry you always are, and you must eat especially well today, to be ready for the long flight."

"Thank you," said Grayling Goose politely. But do you know, that little goose who was always so hungry could not eat a single bite!

Along the Flyway

GRAYLING AND HIS FAMILY are Canada Geese, but there are many other wild geese that also migrate southward from the Arctic to spend the winter months in milder climates.

Even the big gray Canada Geese do not all fly south together. That is just as well, because more than three million of them start out each autumn for the south. Several thousand geese often fly together in one flock.

Some go to Florida, some to Louisiana's low marshland, and others as far west as California. Other flocks of wild geese fly south to the British Isles and Germany. In Asia, many fly over the very high Himalayan Mountains to winter in northern India.

Among some kinds of birds, the grown-ups go on ahead, and the youngsters follow later by themselves. Geese like to fly as families. The mothers and fathers stay together for life, and share in the upbringing of the youngsters.

Geese fly mainly at night; after seventy-five miles or so they stop wherever they find a convenient field that looks as if it can provide a meal. The meal may be of pond weeds or marsh grass. It may be clover or alfalfa, or even part of a farmer's crop of grain.

In built-up parts of the country, wild geese may spend a day near a town. Families of geese, with Mother leading the way and Father on guard bringing up the rear, have been seen making their way across the streets of small northern towns.

One family recently had its picture in many newspapers. It was crossing a street in single file at a traffic stop sign. Cars and trucks waited politely for the family of geese to go by.

Big Ears, the Different Deer

BIG EARS was happy. The sun was shining. She had feasted her fill. Now she kicked up her big hoofs. Her long legs sent her flying across the tundra at a floppy kind of speed.

All around her the reindeer herd was feeding quietly. There was plenty of grass for them to eat. Some of it was already ripening into fuzzy white cotton heads. Big Ears didn't know that people called this cotton grass "reindeer grass," but she did know that she liked the tickly feel of its softness on her nose.

There were plenty of berries on the low, scraggly bushes of the bog land. People might call them blueberries, crowberries, cloudberries or cranberries. Big Ears did not think about their names. But she did like the sweet spicy taste of the juicy berries.

There were green leaves, too, on small bushes and trees. Big Ears did not think about what they were, but she liked to strip

the green leaves from a twig with one sweep of her tongue. They helped to fill her empty tummy. And Big Ears was hungry most of the time, for she was growing fast.

She was growing faster than most of the reindeer yearlings. It was not only her ears that were bigger than most of her playmates'. Her legs were longer. Her broad, flat hoofs, that let her bound so lightly over the spongy bog, were wider. Even the spikes on her brow, where antlers would grow some day, were longer and sharper than most.

Big Ears did not care. She knew that she was a bit different from the rest. She didn't know it was because her father had been a wild caribou. But she did know that the sun was shining, there was plenty to eat and water to drink in every hollow of the marsh. Yes, the world seemed a lovely place to Big Ears that arctic September day.

"Don't wander too far," her mother grunted with a lazy toss of her head.

Reindeer mothers do not worry much about their young. They do not need to. There are so many hundreds of deer in a herd that a youngster could scarcely wander out of sight of all of them. And Big Ears was a yearling, not a calf anymore. She was old enough to look out for herself.

There were people, too, camped somewhere not far away, Big Ears' mother knew. They kept a watchful eye on the deer, and guarded against bold wolves on the prowl. They led the herd from pasture to pasture as the arctic seasons turned. So the mother reindeer, like the yearlings and calves, could relax and enjoy a time of feasting under the late summer sun.

Big Ears' mother was having such a pleasant time that she did not notice how far her youngster was wandering. Big Ears flip-flopped across the tundra. She kicked up her heels as she passed the sod hut where the people camped, and she soon left it far behind. She flicked her ears at a cloud of black flies buzzing by and swiped with her forefeet at places where they bit. She swished her tongue at some late summer flowers. Then she stopped and stared.

Far across the tundra she saw some strange calves and yearlings playing. They were frolicking, kicking up their hoofs just as Big Ears loved to do. And their hoofs were as wide, their legs as long—even their ears were as big as hers!

Slowly Big Ears moved toward the strangers. She felt she must make friends here. When they saw her, they made signs that meant, "Come and play with us." So she kicked up her hoofs and flapped her ears, and hurried to join in their game.

Now that it was September, the days were growing shorter in the Arctic. Soon the sun glowed red along the western horizon, and gray night crept up the eastern sky. It was then that Big Ears heard a deep voice beside her.

"Grumph!" said the deep voice, not unkindly. And a big nose nudged her side.

It was a bull that spoke, a bull much larger than any Big Ears had ever seen. He wore a brown coat, with long winter guard hairs poking through its smooth sheen. A heavy white ruff of long hair on his chest and shoulders made him seem even bigger and heavier than he was. And above each wide rounded hoof he wore a band of white.

The bulls in the reindeer herd where Big Ears belonged were also growing their heavy winter coats. They wore white neck ruffs, too. But they were not as handsome as this.

And the antlers that waved above his brow! Big Ears could not take her eyes off them. They were magnificent. They stood out like the bare, curving branches of a tree, nearly as wide from tip to tip as the bull was tall!

While Big Ears stared, the bull stalked around the circle, nudging the other yearlings and grunting as he went. They gave up their game and began to move quietly. They kept just ahead of the nudging nose and those broad, waving antlers of Great Bull.

Soon Big Ears found herself in a huddle of cows, yearlings and calves. These cows were not nearly as large as the bull, but they were larger than Big Ears' mother and the rest of the cows of the reindeer herd. Their gray neck ruffs were handsomer, Big Ears thought. And they too had long legs and big ears like her own.

"Where are we going?" Big Ears asked as the whole group kept moving under the restless prodding of the bull.

"Don't worry," a kind-eyed cow answered. "Great Bull will decide where we should go."

Soon they climbed over a slight rise of ground, and Big Ears saw, not far ahead, the wide, cold waters of an arctic river.

She remembered with a shiver a river like this from the long journey south a year ago. She had been a young calf then. When the herd came north in the spring, the rivers were still frozen, and the reindeer could walk across them on the ice. But at summer's end, after months of warm sun, the waters stretched deep and wide.

Last year the herd had stopped at the bank, Big Ears remembered, bulls and all, grunting and fussing. They did not want to step in.

At last the people threw a rope around the neck of the largest bull, the leader of the herd. They pushed out into the middle of the river in a boat, pulling the unhappy bull after them. Soon he started to swim, and others, seeing this, followed him. Big Ears and her mother had swum with the rest, though they did not like it very much.

Remembering that river, Big Ears wondered why this Great Bull was heading for the water without any people to push or drag him in.

"The Great Bull seems to be leading us toward that wide river," Big Ears said to the friendly cow.

"What does it matter?" said the cow. "Our winter coats help hold us up. Just paddle with your hoofs as hard as you can, and you will find that you make good time."

Now the dozen cows and yearlings had reached the riverside. Big Ears was surprised to see them enter the water almost without prodding from the bull. They floated high in the water, supported by the hollow, air-filled guard hairs of their winter coats.

Big Ears found herself joining them. At first the cold of the water made her grunt. But she held her head high and paddled her hoofs as hard as she could. She kept up with the group without any trouble. By the time they walked ashore on the far side, shaking their dripping coats, Big Ears was in high spirits again.

"Is there a people's camp around here?" she asked the friendly cow.

"People!" grunted the cow. "We stay away from them. They trap us or shoot us if they can."

"But don't you belong to one of the people's herds?" Big Ears asked in surprise.

"No," said the cow. She gave her antlers a scornful toss. "We caribou belong to no man. For the moment we follow our leader. Later, in the dark of winter, Great Bull will leave us and go off with the other bulls. Then we will join with some other cows. For the cold of winter makes the wolves bold, and there is safety in being together."

"But you never trek south to the people's corral? Then what do you eat when the snow is deep?" Big Ears asked.

"We eat what we find," the cow said proudly. "We do not need people to give us food. We dig holes in the snow, no matter how deep. We dig with our feet until we find moss or dry grass or tasty lichens."

Now Great Bull, who kept restlessly circling the cows, calves and yearlings, spoke once again to Big Ears.

"You are not a tame reindeer," he grunted. "With your splendid long legs and your fine big feet and your nice big ears, you are a true, wild, free caribou. Next spring you will grow wide, beautiful antlers. You will travel proudly across the tundra, bowing to no man."

"I belong to a herd," Big Ears started to say. "I should be getting back." But the Great Bull bent his heavy neck and nudged her gently on.

Big Ears felt a little thrill of excitement. "I wonder what it's like to be free," she thought. She looked back once the way she had come. She could not even see the reindeer herd on the horizon any more. And that wide river flowed between. . . .

"Well," she thought, "I am a caribou now. I'm no longer a 'different' reindeer."

And her big hoofs kicked out in a happy dance as she hurried to join her new friends.

Note: The nomadic peoples of the Arctic, the Lapps, Yakuts and Eskimos, do lose many reindeer from their herds, lured away by wild bands of their cousins the caribou.

Desert and Prairie

WHEN YOU first look out across a wide expanse of desert, it will probably seem both beautiful and strange. Very likely it will seem to be a dead and empty land. You will see a few plants, but most of them will be grayish in tone rather than bright green. Most of them will not even have "real" leaves. This is because broad leaves send out moisture into the air, and desert plants do not have any moisture to spare. A desert is a land with very little rain.

In place of leaves, many desert plants have thin spines that cannot release much precious moisture. They have thick stems to hold whatever moisture they do get.

Animal families that live in the desert have had to develop ways of living without water, too. Some have learned, down through the ages, to make water in their bodies from dry foods they eat.

It is not easy for animals to find enough to eat in the desert. You may not see many

of them searching for food, because many desert animals sleep through most of the hot, sunny days. They come out for food only during the cooler nights. As is true everywhere, the desert has some animals that eat plants. It has others that must hunt living things for meat to eat.

Many of the plant eaters are rodents—kangaroo rats, pocket mice, ground squirrels that scamper about keeping a sharp eye out for enemies as they hunt for nourishing seeds.

The deer family are plant eaters, too, and some of them manage to live in high deserts, along with wild sheep such as the bighorns. These bighorns have rock-gripping pads on their hoofs that enable them to walk up sheer walls of rock.

Meat eaters of the desert include reptiles like the rattlesnake, birds like the owl, and big wild cats.

All these families have cousins living in other kinds of countryside. For example, near many deserts there are wide sunny plains that grow good grass but not many trees. They are called by different names in different lands—veld, savanna, prairie. They are not as dry as deserts, but often in the summer they are very hot. Cousins of most desert animals live on the wide prairies.

If the rains fail in country like this for many years, or the grass is burned or plowed away, the soil becomes dry and powdery. Then winds can blow the soil away, and the land may gradually turn to bare desert. But even in the bleakest desert, if you look closely, you will find some life.

The Prairie Dogs' New Home

"WE MUST have a new home," Mrs. Prairie Dog announced one day.

When Mrs. Prairie Dog sat back on her heels, folded her paws across her chest and made a statement like that, Mr. Prairie Dog always groaned deep inside his chest. He knew it would mean extra work for him.

"A new home!" he said now. "But why, Mother? We have everything we need here. We've just finished fixing it all up."

Mrs. Prairie Dog looked around her. It was impossible to see much of the prairie dogs' home from any one spot. In the first place, it was very dark inside. In the second place, it consisted of a charming tangle of tunnels and burrows with very few straight lines to look along. Some tunnels curved up to back doors. Others led to rounded bedrooms furnished with cozy grass nests.

In the room where Mr. Prairie Dog had been enjoying a peaceful nap, a supply of grass stalks was stored. This room, which Mr. Prairie Dog liked to call his den, was situated just off the guardroom near the front door.

The guardroom was called that because from it one could hear any approaching danger. One—usually Mr. Prairie Dog—could quickly kick up earth to close the tunnel beyond for a little while. This permitted the children to escape by one of the several back doors.

A sloping passage of smooth, hard-packed earth led up from the guardroom to the front doorway. Mr. Prairie Dog was proud of that doorway. It was well located, in the best section of Prairie Town. It was circled by a handsome earth wall as tall as Mr. Prairie Dog. He had just finished strengthening that wall. It was a nice place to sit in the sun, chatting with neighbors. How could Mrs. Prairie Dog seriously think of leaving all this? Mr. Prairie Dog sighed. He knew Mrs. Prairie Dog's strength of will.

"There have been hawks flying over here every day lately," Mrs. Prairie Dog complained. "I scarcely feel safe letting the children play in our own dooryard. Some of the neighbors have seen a sneaky ferret around the neighborhood. And burrowing owls are moving in all over. Anyway, we need more room. I want to move out to the edge of town and have a nice big house. I'll show you the place."

Mr. Prairie Dog gave up the idea of a nap. He stretched and yawned, and he grumbled a little under his breath. But he followed his wife up the front hall to the doorway.

Out in the sunshine, he began to feel better. The town was alive with chattering and chirping. You could hear a little of everyone's business, just walking down the street.

Mrs. Prairie Dog was not wasting time on gossip just now. She led the way briskly through Prairie Town to the outskirts. There she stopped at a pleasant, open bit of land and waved a paw around. Mr. Prairie Dog was pleased to find that it was not really so very far from his old home.

"Very well," he said. "I'll start digging."

And he did. With Mrs. Prairie Dog supervising, he had soon built a handsome round doorway with a large walled yard outside. Inside the doorway a nicely sloping hallway led to a new guardroom. Mr. Prairie Dog left a space undug off to the left. He secretly planned to build himself a den there, even nicer than the old one, as soon as he had time. For the moment he concentrated on cozy round bedrooms for all the family.

When the new home was ready, even Mr. Prairie Dog had to admit that he was

pleased. The children squealed with delight as they raced around exploring all the new tunnels. They were pleased to find their own grass beds set up in the new bedrooms.

"It all smells so lovely and new!" they cried, as they raced out one back door and in another.

"Well," said Mr. Prairie Dog to his wife, "I hope you're satisfied."

"There's a lot to be done before we'll really be settled," she said. "We still need more rooms. But those can come later. I'm glad we're moved, anyway."

The next time they went back to the old neighborhood to visit friends and neighbors and the children's old playmates, they found that a family of burrowing owls had already moved into their former home.

"There were a few things I left there that I'd like to have," fussed Mrs. Prairie Dog. "But I guess they just couldn't wait."

"We like the new house better," said the children as the family started home.

They all felt proud and happy when

they saw the wall of the new dooryard ahead. But what was this? Their neighbors were sounding an alarm with sharp, quick cries. Soon the family were close enough to peek into the dooryard. And there, in the nice round dooryard that Mr. Prairie Dog had patted smooth with so much care, lay something strange.

"A rattlesnake!" barked Father Prairie Dog. "Stay away, children!"

The children clung to their parents' legs, trembling with fright. They had no desire to go anywhere near the rattlesnake, even if its head was hidden from sight down inside the house. They had heard dreadful stories as long as they could remember about rattlers' poison fangs.

"What shall we do! Where can we go? What about our new house?" they cried.

"Don't worry," said Father Prairie Dog, drawing himself up tall and proud. "I'll dig us a place to camp for the night. Tomorrow the rattlesnake may be gone if it finds there's no one at home."

Father Prairie Dog found a vacant plot back near their old home. Swiftly he set to work. First he dug a good tunnel, kicking out the dirt with his strong hind paws. Mrs.

Prairie Dog showed the children how to pack the dirt into the beginning of a new dooryard wall.

By the time the moon rose over the prairie, Father Prairie Dog had a nice big room dug at the end of the new tunnel. While he watched the children, Mother Prairie Dog cut some grass for new beds.

"We think it's fun to camp out," said the children as they curled up together in one big grass bed.

Their parents were too tired to speak. They only gave a weary sigh.

As soon as the sun's first rays slanted across Prairie Town next morning, Father Prairie Dog scampered down the street to the new house to see if the rattlesnake had left.

"Too late! Too late!" said the neighbor next door, who was sitting on his own dooryard wall enjoying the morning sun. "A family of cottontail rabbits has just moved in."

Father Prairie Dog barked at the front door. No one came. Then he ran around to one of his back doors. There, sure enough, in the shade of a sage bush, sat Mother Cottontail. She was giving her chubby babies

a lesson in washing their faces and combing their long whiskers with their paws.

"Sorry, this is my house!" said Father Prairie Dog in his sternest bark.

Mrs. Cottontail just blinked her eyes and shrugged her shoulders prettily. She did not understand prairie-dog talk!

At last Father Prairie Dog gave up and walked away.

"Is it all right now? Can we go home?" the children called as soon as they saw him.

"No," said Father Prairie Dog with a sigh. "I think I'll just settle down and build us another new home here."

So once again Mr. Prairie Dog set to work, digging more tunnels and burrows this way and that. Meanwhile, Mrs. Prairie Dog took the children out to look for food.

"The worst of this," Father Prairie Dog told himself sadly as he worked, "is that I'll be digging tunnels and building rooms forever at this rate. I'll never have time to fix myself a nice little den like the one I had back in the old place." He thought longingly of those peaceful naps as he dug and kicked and patted away.

He had finished about half the rooms and tunnels Mrs. Prairie Dog had asked for when something strange happened. His paw went through a wall into open space, instead of into solid ground. He had dug into a room of another house!

"Pardon me!" Mr. Prairie Dog called to whoever might be there, and he started to back out.

No one answered. That made Mr. Prairie Dog curious, so he decided to peek through the hole he had made.

Dark as it was, he noticed two things. First, he could not hear a sound. There did not seem to be anyone there. Second, the place did not smell as if anyone lived there. It smelled empty.

76

As he puzzled over this, a third thought came to him. There was something familiar about that empty room. He felt that he had been there before.

Wiping his paws clean, Mr. Prairie Dog stepped through the hole in the wall, into the room he had stumbled upon. It was a good-sized room, with a tunnel leading away from it, of course. He followed the tunnel. Still there was not a sound, nor a sign of anyone living there.

The farther he went, the more at home Mr. Prairie Dog felt. At last his nose carried him around a turn, and there he was in his dear old den! He had stumbled into his own old home!

Where were the burrowing owls who had moved in when he and his family moved out? Mr. Prairie Dog searched every tunnel. There was not a sign of them. At last he made his way up the sloping front hall and popped his head out his own old front door.

At once he was greeted by his neighbor on the left.

"Glad to see you back!"

"What has become of the burrowing owls?" asked Mr. Prairie Dog.

"Moved out to the edge of town," said the neighbor with a wave of his paw. "They heard there was a nice new house that was vacant out there. A cottontail rabbit family was moving out of it. Seems Mrs. Cottontail didn't speak any prairie-dog talk and she got too lonesome to stay."

"No!" groaned Mr. Prairie Dog. But then his face brightened.

Now Mrs. Prairie Dog would have a house with all the rooms she could possibly ask for, with lots of back tunnels and two front doors. And he would have his own den, just for himself. At the thought of it, Mr. Prairie Dog hurried right back there and curled up for a nice peaceful nap.

Tom Tortoise's Trouble

TOM TORTOISE was in trouble. You would not have known it to look at him. He marched about the rocky desert with all his usual dignity. His head nodded slightly as he lumbered along. Now and then he paused to munch a berry or a leaf. Seeing him, you might have thought Tom didn't have a trouble in the world. But he did. He didn't know where he was!

If you are a dignified desert fellow, this is a difficult thing to admit. Of course you know where you are! Very likely, if you are a desert tortoise, you travel every day in a circular pattern within the same small stretch of desert.

Tom Tortoise's territory lay in the area where he had always lived, between the big red rock and the clump of sage brush and the Joshua tree.

There was never any reason for him to leave home. There were plenty of thick-stemmed desert plants around for him to nibble on. They held enough rich juice to fill the water sacs beneath his tortoise shell. This supply carried him through the long dry spells.

Tom had a shallow burrow to call his home, and a wide desert outside under a sunny sky. Why should he travel farther, when right at home he had everything a desert tortoise could ask for?

That was the way Tom Tortoise felt. So he had stayed pretty close to the spot where he had hatched from a tough-skinned, round white egg. That hatching had been some time ago, so Tom Tortoise knew his home desert very well. But where in the world was he now?

There were rocks aplenty. That he could see as he swung his head this way and that. But not his big red rock. There were bushes enough, but no purple sage like the clump that marked his home territory. There were thick-stemmed cactus plants on which to chew, but not a single long-armed Joshua tree in sight.

Where in the world was he?

Tom plodded wearily round and round in

the sun, trying to find something he knew, until he was tired and hot. Then he found himself a strip of shade beside a big gray-green rock and settled down to try to think.

He could remember coming out of his burrow, out of its cool darkness into the bright sun. He had known just where he wanted to go, so he wasted no time. He had plodded carefully along, stepping just on the claws of his flipperlike front feet, but planting his back feet solidly. *Plod, plod, plod,* he had made his slow and sober way over to the big Joshua tree.

That was where he had met the lady tortoise. She had seemed very friendly, Tom remembered. Tom Tortoise was inclined to be shy. He was glad to have made a friend.

Just as they passed beyond the stage of nodding acquaintance, though, something happened. Tom felt something lift his shell, first from one side, then from the other. He kicked his short legs out as hard as he could. Whatever it was would not let go. And he could not touch the ground!

This was bad. Tom knew only one way to protect himself. He pulled his legs and head deep inside the hard case of his shell.
78

As he waited there, he heard strange sounds that did not belong on his desert. But Tom did not poke out his head to see where the sounds came from. He felt himself land on something hard. But Tom did not poke out a leg to feel what the hard thing was.

Then for a long time he was jounced and tumbled. It reminded Tom of a fight he had once had as a young tortoise.

That had been a narrow escape. And ever since that long-ago time Tom had lived a very quiet life. Until now. Not knowing where he was was very upsetting.

The strange jouncing and tumbling journey in the dark was a long one, but at least Tom could breathe as he was bounced about. Now and then he heard what sounded like a clash of shell on shell. Perhaps there were other tortoises here, too! Once Tom did peek out, but there was nothing to see but blackness, so he pulled in his head again and went to sleep.

He had no idea that he was riding in the back of a pickup truck. He had no idea that his capture was part of a People Plan. Tom Tortoise had never heard of People. Even if he had heard the men talking up in the cab of the truck, he would not have understood.

"How many do we have this trip?" one of the men asked as the truck bounded over a rough stretch of road.

"Eight," said the driver.

"How many will there be?"

"A hundred or more, we think," said the driver. "The Boy Scouts are checking the desert along this whole stretch of highway. We know there are tortoises living all through this country, but no one knows just how many."

"Do they all have to be moved?" the rider asked. He was a newcomer.

"Well," said the driver, "we don't want tortoises wandering onto the road and being killed. We can't expect them to know about roads and automobiles, so we'll have to round them all up and relocate them."

"What happens to them when we dump them where we're going?"

"They should do just fine. It's desert country like their old home. All they have to do is dig themselves new burrows and make themselves at home."

The truck driver sounded as if it would all be very simple. But it didn't seem simple to Tom when he woke up as he was tumbled out of the truck onto the gravelly desert, with the sun beating down on his shell.

Tom liked warmth and sunshine as well as the next tortoise, but this heat soon got to be too much for him. When his head cleared, after all the jouncing, he poked out his feet and pushed out his head and started for his burrow and some cool shade.

That was when Tom realized he was in trouble. He could not find his burrow, his very own burrow that he had dug all by himself! He searched for hours, but he still could not find anything in the world that he had ever seen before!

Tom shook his head slowly in puzzlement. It was then he caught a glimpse of a familiar-looking shell over near a big cactus.

Tom sniffed the air. It seemed a little cooler than it had before. So, setting his weight on the claws of his forepaws, he started out in his sober *plod, plod, plodding* way.

Before he reached the big cactus he was sure. It was the lady tortoise he had met back home. Tom nodded to her, and she nodded back. She seemed glad to see him. As she started slowly toward him, Tom began to feel happier inside.

The lady tortoise was as troubled as Tom.

79

She did not know what had happened, but now that she had met a friend, she was sure that everything would be all right.

"This seems a nice location," Tom told her. "Come along and I'll show you some very tasty leaves. There's even a little mudhole down beyond those rocks. I found it as I was—er, scouting around." He began to be glad of all the time he had spent wandering about so unhappily. For now he could be her guide.

"I can't even find my own burrow," the lady tortoise said.

"Don't worry," said Tom, with a wise nod of his head. "I'll show you just the spot to dig a new one. In fact, I'll help you. I'll be glad to. It will be no trouble at all."

And do you know, from that time on Tom Tortoise's troubles were over. Thanks to the lady tortoise, he soon felt very much at home. He and she had a new territory. They traveled each day in a circular path between the big gray-green rock and the mudhole and the big cactus plant. And Tom was very happy in his *plod, plod, plodding* way.

Note: There really is a desert highway being built through tortoise country. And there really is a Great Tortoise Roundup going on. The plan is to pick up all the tortoises as they leave their burrows. This will keep them from wandering onto the new road and being killed. They are being transported to a section of desert where there are no roads, and where they can safely make new homes. Let us hope that they all, like Tom Tortoise, will find friends there.

80

When the Earth Shook

It was quiet and peaceful on the desert in the middle of a sunny day. All the nighttime hunters were asleep, curled up somewhere in the shade. Horned Owl slept with his head hunched into one wing. Kid Coyote no longer howled at the moon. He was fast asleep under a thorny bush, dreaming of plump jackrabbits for dinner. Kit Fox was in his burrow, safe from the heat.

Pancho Lizard sat all by himself on a sun-warmed rock and blinked a sleepy eye.

"This is the life," said the lazy little lizard, with a flick of his long green tail. "Nothing to do, because I've eaten my fill of delicious blossoms. No hungry hunters to dodge. Nowhere to go, because I'm just where I want to be. And nothing around to bother me."

Suddenly the warm rock beneath him shivered. *BONG-bong-de-bong-bong!* A distant noise shook the little lizard from his happy doze. Pancho raised up on his front legs with a start.

"An earthquake!" he thought. "I had better be moving!"

So off went Pancho, as fast as he could go, across the dry and sun-warmed desert.

Not far away, in the shade of a purple sage bush, Georgie Ground Squirrel sat.

Behind him stretched the cool doorway of his burrow. Before him spread the wide, sunny desert.

"This is the life," said the plump young squirrel to himself. He folded his forepaws over his round middle. "Plenty of tasty seeds at paw's reach. No hunters to bother me while the sun shines. Nothing to do but sit in the shade—or in the sun, if I want."

Just then the purple sage bush shivered, and its dry leaves rattled.

BONG-bong-de-bong-bong!

Georgie jumped up with a start and rubbed his astonished eyes.

All around, the desert was still dozing in the sun. But wait! Here came a small dust cloud rolling along. At the front of the small cloud raced Pancho Lizard, hurrying as fast as his short legs could go, while his long tail stirred up the cloud behind.

"What is it?" called Georgie Ground Squirrel.

"An earthquake!" called Pancho. When he reached Georgie's sage bush he didn't even pause. He just called back over his shoulder, "You had better come along."

So off went Georgie Ground Squirrel after Pancho Lizard, as fast as his round little tummy would permit him to run.

81

Not far away, in the shade of a creosote bush, Jack Rabbit was taking his ease.

"This is the life," said lazy Jack, stretching his long hind legs. "Nothing to do but rest," he said, "and nothing to bother me." He slowly waved his long ears to stir up a bit of breeze.

Just then the scraggly bush quivered above his head. *BONG-bong-de-bong-bong!* A noise like none Jack Rabbit had ever heard before echoed through the heat waves that danced across the sunny desert land.

Jack Rabbit leaped into the air with one bound of his long hind legs.

Along came Pancho Lizard and Georgie Ground Squirrel, traveling as fast as a storm cloud sails across the sky.

"What is it?" called Jack Rabbit.

"The earth is quaking!" cried Georgie. "You had better come with us."

Jack Rabbit flipped his whiskers and flexed his hind legs. Then off he went, *lippity clippity zip!*

Beyond a rise of desert ground, run-away Painted Pony rolled on the warm desert and whinnied for joy.

"This is the life," said he. "No rider to carry, no load to pull. Oh, the peaceful, empty desert. This is the place for me."

Suddenly the ground beneath him shivered. *BONG-bong-de-bong-bong!* The peaceful silence was shattered by the sound.

Painted Pony rolled to his knees and staggered to his feet with a start.

Then up raced Jack Rabbit, who was now ahead of Pancho Lizard and Georgie Ground Squirrel. All three were out of breath.

"What is it?" neighed Painted Pony.

"The earth is quaking!" said Jack Rabbit.

"You had better come with us," gasped Georgie Ground Squirrel.

Pancho Lizard, who had been running longest, could only wave his weary tail.

"Jump on my back!" cried Painted Pony.

That was easier said than done. It was easy enough for Jack Rabbit. Up he went with a bound. Then he reached down one long leg to Georgie Ground Squirrel. But poky Pancho Lizard had to crawl slowly all the way up Painted Pony's long thick tail.

As soon as all three were safe on his back, away went Painted Pony, half as fast as the wind when it whistles down out of the far blue hills.

Some distance ahead, on a low hilltop, sat Straight Arrow, an American Indian boy. Between his knees he held a fine new skin-covered drum.

When he saw a round dust cloud come rolling across the desert, Straight Arrow lifted his hands from the drum and used them to shade his eyes.

Then he could see Painted Pony galloping

along, with Pancho Lizard and Georgie Ground Squirrel and Jack Rabbit on his back.

"What a sight to see!" said young Straight Arrow to himself. "I thought Painted Pony would grow tired of running away. I hoped he would come back. But I never dreamed he would come like this. My friends will never believe it!"

He put his hands to his mouth and called, "Ho, Painted Pony, I'm over here!"

Painted Pony was glad to hear a voice he knew. He was glad to see Straight Arrow again. So he changed his course and galloped over to the low hill.

"What's the matter?" Straight Arrow asked when he saw the foam that flecked Painted Pony's mouth and the wild, frightened look in his eye.

Painted Pony neighed. And he pawed with one hoof until small stones rattled and the riders on his back all shivered and shook as though there were an earthquake.

"The earth is quaking?" laughed Straight Arrow, who knew Painted Pony very well and understood him, too. "You mean the BONG-bong-de-bong-bong? That was just me and my new drum!"

And he sat down and beat out, firm and loud, BONG-bong-de-bong-bong with the flat of his brown hands.

The warm rocks shivered in the sun. The cottonwood trees shivered along the dry stream bed. The creosote bushes quivered to

the tips of their twigs. And the dry earth shook beneath their feet.

"We made the earthquake!" laughed Straight Arrow. "My splendid drum and I!"

Then they all laughed with him. Pancho Lizard and Georgie Ground Squirrel and Jack Rabbit laughed so hard that they rolled off Painted Pony's back. Painted Pony put his nose into Straight Arrow's hand and whinnied loud with joy.

They laughed until the very air shook with the happy sound. And the little dust clouds rolled away laughing across the desert sands.

Who Eats What?

SOME PEOPLE think meat-eating animals are fierce and cruel because they hunt and kill other animals to feed themselves and their families. Coyotes and wolves have a bad reputation. Foxes are considered thieves when they take a chicken for their young.

Animals such as rabbits and deer that live on plants seem gentler, somehow "nicer." But this is scarcely fair, for each animal eats the food its system needs. And each has a place in the chain of life.

On land, insects are the smallest link in the animal chain. Some of them eat plants, and others such as mosquitoes and flies—and some spiders—like to suck the blood of animals. They may even nip at us! There are insects that like to nibble our clothes and the paper in our books.

Many small animals—such as most birds, and reptiles like lizards and turtles—eat insects. Others, such as the squirrel family, prefer nuts and seeds and roots of plants. Rabbits like to nibble roots and leaves. If the plants they nibble are in our gardens, we do not like this.

Hunters such as owls, hawks and eagles among the birds, and the cat and dog families among ground animals, need meat. They hunt mice, ground squirrels, rabbits, deer and other animals.

Sometimes the animals they hunt belong to people. Eagles may swoop down and at-

tack sick or wounded lambs. Wild cats like cougars, bob cats, lynxes, tigers and lions may kill cattle. Then the people who raise the sheep or cattle for a living are angry. They feel they must hunt and kill the eagles or wild cats.

In some areas, families of wild cats have almost been wiped out by hunters. Then the deer and rabbits on which they feed grow up undisturbed. Soon there are so many of them that they cannot find enough plants to eat. Many of them starve for lack of food.

Left to themselves, the meat eaters and the plant eaters keep things in balance. There are insects whose work it is to clean up dead plants and animals. They put the materials that made up those plants and animals back into the soil. Then it can be used again to make plants grow. The plants can feed insects and reptiles and small mammals, and the chain of life is kept complete.

Each animal, given a chance, does its part. Even the fiercest hunters among the large mammals—excepting possibly the killer whale—do not kill other creatures just for fun. They hunt to eat, to feed their families or to protect them from danger. Strangely enough, it is only Man who kills for fun. How sad it is to realize he has destroyed many kinds of birds and animals so that not a single one of their kind remains.

Marsh, Pond and Bog

WHEREVER YOU LIVE, there is probably some damp marshland not very many miles away. It is found in all climates, hot and cold. There are arctic marshes in treeless lands where both land and water are frozen most of the year. There are tropical swamps so overgrown with bushes and tall trees that sunlight scarcely touches their dark pools.

There are salt or tide marshes near most seacoasts. There the sea water creeps up the streams and over the low land when the tide is in. There are bogs in hollows in many woods, spongy land where open lakes once lay.

Most people do not care to live in marshy land because the air is so damp and so many insects live there. People who do live in very low, wet country often build their homes up on stilts to keep them out of the water. They keep small boats at their front doors or tucked under their front porches.

A swamp or marsh is a very good place for birds to live. You may hear the flutelike call of the thrush or the piping of a sparrow

in a bog in the woods. An arctic marsh may be loud with the wing-beat of thousands of ducks, geese and terns. In a steaming warm swamp you may see long-legged cranes, egrets, herons and lovely coral-pink flamingos.

There are many birds that want to live near water. Baby ducks learn to swim—in a straight line behind their mother—as soon as they learn to walk on their wide, webbed feet.

A marsh also has many plants that grow their seeds inside round, tasty berries. Birds like these. And the tall grasses grow crisper seeds at their tips, which birds like to nibble. There are many, many insects buzzing around a swamp, and many of them provide tasty food for birds.

"Insects taste good to me, too," croaks a frog. He blinks his bulging eyes and flicks out his long, swift tongue to catch a flying insect in midair. Along with frogs and toads, turtles like to live in marshes and bogs. They like to lie on logs in the sun and snap at insects flying by. There are also larger animals to be found—muskrats, otters, and in warm countries alligators or crocodiles. They like a diet of meat.

In many swamps there are even plants that eat meat—insects, at least. Tiny sundew plants actually reach out thin tentacles like arms to catch insects. Bladderworts, plants with a strange name, wait until an insect lights. Then suction pulls the small creature in, and a trap door closes behind it.

The pitcher plant attracts insects with a delicious smell. But when the insect lands, it finds its feet slipping out from under it. Down a slippery slide it goes, into the "pitcher" full of a sort of thick soup which the plant uses for food.

Many of these marsh plants grow out over the waters of shallow lakes or ponds. They

may grow on a floating mat made of the stems and roots of other summers' growth. Each year more root-threads are woven into the mat, and more fallen stems add to its soft carpet. Gradually these floating mats can support bigger plants. Bushes like the bog laurel may grow on them, putting out tiny flowers in the spring and reaching down, down, down with their roots.

Many roots reach through the lake or pond water to poke their way into the mud bottom. After some years the mat no longer floats. It is anchored to the bottom by roots. A place where the soft, spongy soil is made up mainly of old plants is called a bog.

It takes many years for bog plants to inch their way out from the edges toward the center of a pond. While there is still some open water, loons and terns, wild geese and other birds will swoop down to a landing on the still, black water at twilight. They will find plenty of food. In the morning they will be on their way again, southward in the autumn, northward in the spring.

Behind them, the plants reach out farther over the pond with each passing year. Flying dust is caught and settles to form some soil. Mosses fill the spaces between the stems and roots. Trees tumbled by storms or worn by rot fall into the mat and decay. Very slowly new land is built up where a lake or pond once lay. It is spongy and uneven, often bulging up in small rounded hummocks.

"A bog is a bad place to walk," people say. "It quakes and shakes. It may have holes where your foot goes down into water. And oh, my, the insects!"

The bog is a halfway stage in Nature's process of building new land. Meanwhile, it makes a good, quiet home for many birds and animals. And oh, my, how swarms of insects do flourish in a bog!

Little Mole
Sees the World

LITTLE MOLE'S HOME was a burrow deep underground. That was where he lived, night and day. The world was all darkness to Little Mole.

Oh, his home did have a doorway that led Outside. This small doorway was tucked under the root of a big stump that stood close beside the swamp. But Little Mole's family did not think much of the world Outside.

Home to them was a cozy dark round room lined with dead leaves and grass. It was warm in winter and cool in summer. And it had a firm, well-built tunnel leading to it.

Father Mole was proud of that tunnel. He had put a lot of work into it, because digging a tunnel nearly two feet underground is hard work even for a good digger like a mole.

Of course, Father and Mother Mole and Little Mole did not spend all their time at home. They had to eat, and eating, to a mole, means tunneling after food. It's not just a little snack a mole has in mind when he thinks of eating. Moles like to eat a third to half their weight in food every day.

Earthworms were Little Mole's favorite food. But the dark underground also held ants and the baby larvae of insects and spiders; there were centipedes and millipedes and lots of special treats.

All the moles had to do to find a meal was to branch out from their main tunnel and dig. Little Mole had learned to do this before he was two months old.

He was splendidly built for digging. He was streamlined, from his soft pointed nose up through his heavy shoulders and back to his small tail. Not even his ears poked out to get in the way. His gray fur coat was so short and velvety that he could go backward or forward in a tunnel without rumpling his fur.

Little Mole did most of his digging with his front feet. They were shaped like shovels, with heavy claws on the toes to tear into the earth.

First he scouted around with his soft nose for a good place to dig. Then he started shoveling dirt with his big front feet. He wriggled his round body as he worked, pushing against the sides and roof of his new tunnel. The dirt he shoveled out he pushed under his tummy and kicked behind him with his small hind feet.

"The most important thing to remember," his father had taught him, "is not to come to the surface."

Little Mole could tell by the weight of the earth above him how close to the world Outside he was. He could tunnel swiftly along just below the surface, quite speedily

and surely, without ever breaking through to the Outside.

He did not know, and his father did not know, that animals and people traveling on top of the ground could see just where the moles' food tunnels went. They were often so close to the surface that the tunnel roofs made long curving humps along the ground. When one of these humps ran across a lawn, this annoyed the people very much. Men muttered crossly about the work of moles.

Father Mole did not care what anyone else thought about his tunnels. He was a solitary soul. He liked to work alone and to be by himself. He was not a very cheerful fellow. He even quarreled with Mother Mole and grumped at Little Mole. And he did not care to make friends.

Now and then one mole tunnel crossed another. And so it happened one day that Little Mole, on the lookout for earthworms, bumped into a strange young mole with a roundish fringe around his soft nose.

"Hello," said the stranger cheerfully. He was a star-nose mole, and the star-noses are more friendly by nature than most other moles.

Little Mole said shyly, "Hello."

"Is this tunnel part of your Mole Town?" asked Star Nose.

"We don't live in a town," whispered Little Mole. "We just live by ourselves down below here in our own deep tunnel and our own cozy home, my mother and father and I. We dig around to find our food. We dig new food tunnels all the time, but they are just for us."

"Don't you ever go Outside?" asked Star Nose.

"Oh, no," said Little Mole. "My mother and father don't believe in that. They say the Outside is a terrible place."

Star Nose laughed. "I go all the time. It's

exciting Outside. Have you never seen the woods or the swamp? Come along with me. I'll show you the world."

Little Mole felt an itch of curiosity in his nose. "All right!" he said. "Let's go."

Star Nose pointed upward and began to dig. Dirt came flying back in Little Mole's face, but he did not mind. He just flipped his own front feet and wriggled his own tummy and sent that dirt flying out behind him.

After a while a glare of light made him squeeze his little eyes shut.

"Wow!" he said. "The dark is easier to look at!"

Soon he could open his eyes again. But Little Mole was used to darkness, and all he could see in the bright Outside was a blur of blue and brown and green.

"Let's go to the swamp," said Star Nose.

Little Mole did not have any trouble following his new friend. His nose told him which way to go, and small hairs on his hands kept him from bumping into things.

Soon his nose told him that water lay ahead. Little Mole drew back.

"Aren't you going to come in swimming?" called Star Nose. Little Mole could hear him splashing happily nearby.

Little Mole reached out one shovel foot and tried the water. "No, thank you," he said.

"You're missing a lot of fun," said Star Nose. "Here, try these." He handed Little Mole a fistful of water bugs.

"They are good," Little Mole admitted when he had eaten them. "But I don't know how to swim."

"Easy," said Star Nose. "All you do is paddle with your feet and steer with your tail. See, like this."

Little Mole heard a great splashing as Star Nose showed off.

"No, thanks," said Little Mole. "Our deep tunnel was flooded once, and we had to paddle through water to get out. I didn't like it a bit."

"Out of my way," said a cross voice behind Little Mole, and someone pushed him.

Little Mole dodged aside, and a small creature not half his size pushed past, sputtering and fussing. Little Mole heard a small splash as the water shrew—for that is what the creature was—popped into the swamp. Then there was no more sound.

Little Mole turned his head to listen. He could hear the rustle of leaves and the creaking of branches on the tall trees overhead. He could hear the roar of the bees buzzing down upon blossoms. Close by he could hear the chomp of cutworms biting into green leaves and the stamp of the centipede's many tiny feet, for moles can hear very well.

"My, it's noisy here in the Outside," thought Little Mole. But not a sound from the water shrew did he hear.

"What became of him?" Little Mole asked Star Nose.

"Oh, he's hunting fish eggs or frog eggs on the bottom," said Star Nose. "Those shrews are good ones to stay away from. They're small, but they have sharp teeth, and their bite is poison!

"Ho, here he comes up again! Water Shrew's fur holds so many tiny drops of air that it never gets wet all the way through, even when he walks on the bottom of the pond," Star Nose explained. "And look at that! He can walk on the water, too. He claims he holds air bubbles on his feet."

Little Mole could only see a blur as the shrew hurried past, but he was impressed.

Suddenly, "Ouch!" he heard Star Nose cry out. "Give me a hand."

Little Mole reached out a sharp-clawed paw. He felt Star Nose snatch at it. He pulled, and soon Star Nose was lying on the bank beside him, puffing to get his breath.

"A big fish got me by the toe!" gasped Star Nose. "You really have to be on guard when you're swimming in the swamp. Fish and turtles can pull you down, and then you're finished."

"The dark Underground is safer than the swamp," said Little Mole.

Then he pointed his little nose into the air. He smelled the sweet fragrance of the swamp blossoms, the sharp rich smell of rotting leaves and wood, and the light, airy scent of a breeze dancing across the pond.

"It doesn't smell at all like home," said Little Mole to himself. "I miss the smell of the nice dark moldy Underground."

Little Mole opened his eyes wider. "Hey," he said. "It's getting easier for me to see. Things aren't as bright anymore."

"Yes," said Star Nose. "Twilight has come. It will soon be dark Outside—not as dark as Underground, but dark." He did not sound pleased. His voice sounded uneasy.

"Isn't that good?" asked Little Mole.

"Well," said Star Nose in a whisper, "lots of big hunters come out at night. There are skunks and foxes that come stealing out of the woods, and hawks and owls that drop from the sky."

"Whew!" said Little Mole. "The Underground doesn't have any of those. My father told me a story once about a snake that came down a tunnel into some mole family's house, but I've never really seen a snake. We don't have many hunters where I live. I guess the good old Underground is the place

for me. But thanks for showing me the world Outside."

Then Little Mole followed his nose to the doorway hidden under the stump. He ran down the tunnel as fast as his stumpy little legs could take him.

When he reached his family's living room, he could hear his parents quarreling.

"Where is that young mole?" his father was fussing. "This is no time for you to let him be out. Day is the time when the earthworms are easy to find."

"I can't watch him every minute," his mother said crossly. "Why don't you look after him some of the time?"

"I'm here," called Little Mole.

"Well," grumped his father. "It's about time. You've had your mother and me worried sick. Where have you been?"

"I've been off with my friend Star Nose," said Little Mole. "I've been Outside to see the world."

"Outside!" cried Mother Mole. "We told you you wouldn't like it."

"Outside," grumbled Father Mole. "You are lucky you got back. It's mighty dangerous up there. Now get some rest. We have a lot of digging to do tomorrow."

"Yes," said Little Mole quietly. "It's better here for a mole." And he settled down to rest.

Next morning Little Mole went quietly back to his digging. He found some delicious plump earthworms and swallowed them down hungrily. He was glad to be back home. And he still is today.

Every once in a while, though, his eyes grow tired of blackness. His ears feel too full of the silence of the Underground. There is nothing to do but *dig, dig, dig*.

Every once in a while, then, Little Mole says to himself with a sigh, "My, it was exciting in that world Outside."

Hector Comes Home

HECTOR ALLIGATOR made his home among the reeds along the shore of a warm and shallow pond. He had hatched from an egg among those reeds. His mother had heaped up a nice, messy nest of leaves, grass, twigs and mud there and had laid her eggs in it. When Hector wriggled out of his shell, he stayed alive by hiding in the tangle of reeds when hungry snakes slithered by or skunks came prowling or a black-masked raccoon pounced.

Little eight-inch baby alligators are a favorite food of many swamp hunters. Not many of Hector's brood lived to grow up. But Hector did.

When he was a little older, Hector learned that he was safer in the water than on shore. He learned to lie underwater, very quietly, with just his nostrils and his bulging eyes above the still surface.

Sometimes he would close his nostrils and ears and sink gently to the bottom of the pond. He could stay there for hours before he needed another breath of air. He found it very restful to let the water lap around him.

If he wanted to move, he could slide through the water without having to support his weight. And one flip of his tail was enough to turn him halfway around.

The best thing about the bottom of the swamp pond was that it was full of food. There were crunchy crabs, tough turtles, whole schools of little fish. Hector never chased them. All he had to do was open his mouth, close his throat with his tongue, and give one good hard swish of his tail. He

would sail forward and his mouth would fill with a delicious meal. Then he would shut his jaws with a snap, let the water drip out between his teeth, and swallow the food.

Hector usually swallowed a few pebbles too. They helped mash up the bones and shells and other parts that might have been hard for his stomach to handle. This work was all done in the first of his two stomachs. But Hector did not have to worry about that. All he had to do was open his mouth, snap shut his jaws, let the extra water dribble out, then open his throat and swallow.

Hector found the swamp pond a very pleasant place to live. He never dreamed of leaving. He probably never would have, but with the years the pond changed.

Hector began to hear hammering and sawing sounds as he lay snoozing in the sunny grass beside the pond. Some People were building a small house nearby. Well, that didn't bother Hector. They cut down some trees and filled in some hollows and planted some different plants. But that didn't bother Hector either, and he didn't bother them.

Then the man came sloshing into the pond and pounded some posts into the muddy bottom. He built himself a little pier and tied a little boat to it. Early in the mornings he would go out on the pond in that little boat and catch a few fish.

There were plenty of fish in the pond. Hector could spare some. So that didn't bother him, either. He found the shadow of the pier a pleasant place to lie and snooze.

The man soon became acquainted with Hector. Since Hector was by this time more than twelve feet long, and weighed about three hundred pounds, he was rather hard to miss.

One morning when the man came out to go fishing he brought a thick slice of bread

95

spread with dogfood for Hector. Hector was willing to try anything once. He opened his jaws, and the man tossed in the bread.

Hector swallowed the bread and blinked his eyes with pleasure. He really liked it.

The next morning the man brought Hector another slice of bread-and-dogfood. Hector flicked his tail appreciatively. The water his tail tossed up soaked the man, but that didn't seem to bother the man any more than it would have bothered Hector. So the two became friends.

Then one morning the man overslept. Hector came swimming up to the pier. He floated around for a while as patiently as he could. Then he let out a bellow that echoed over the pond. The man soon appeared with his snack, you may be sure!

He also added another treat that Hector liked even better than bread-and-dogfood. This was marshmallows served on a long wooden spoon. Hector knew very well there was nothing in the swamp like them.

The two friends enjoyed one another's company on the pond for some time. Then other people began to come. There was more hammering and sawing. More houses went up. More piers poked into the water.

Well, Hector did not really mind as long as they let him alone, but some of his animal neighbors in the swamp did not like living near people. Soon there were not as many muskrats and lizards and otters as there had been. Hector missed them, because they had added variety to his meals when he managed to snap his great jaws on one. But there were still plenty of fish and turtles and crabs. And he still had his morning bread-and-dogfood snack and special treats of marshmallows provided by his friend, the man.

By this time Hector was about sixty years old. He was content just to lie in the sun or

under his friend's pier or at the bottom of the pond and let the world go by.

The new people did not bother Hector. But he bothered them. They did not understand that when he swam up beside their fishing boats and opened his wide, smiling jaws, he was just being friendly. They did not understand that when he let out a bellow in the early morning air he was just reminding his friend that it was time for his bread-and-dogfood lunch.

Yes, Hector bothered the new people. They never stopped to think that this pond had been his home long before they came.

"That alligator has to go," they said. And they did something about it.

Hector did not know that any plan was afoot. He was swimming around his friend's pier one morning as usual when a loop of rope suddenly sang through the air and settled around his jaws. His jaws were closed with a snap, and he could not open them. Then he felt himself being dragged ashore. He was lifted into the back of a truck. And away went Hector Alligator to a state park.

Hector did not know that was the name of the place, but he did know he didn't like it. It wasn't home. There was water enough to swim in. There were fish to eat. There was sun to lie in for a snooze. But though he bellowed his loudest every morning, no one brought him that delicious bread and meat, to say nothing of marshmallows. The new place wasn't home. So Hector started back.

The going was easy enough as long as he could follow the swamp. He swam or just paddled his feet along the bottom, opening his mouth whenever a school of small darting fish swam by. He traveled that way for several days. Then he came to a place where the swamp was crossed by a road.

Hector didn't know it was a road, of course, but he knew something was in his

way. He poked his way into a shady spot and took a long rest before he started climbing the steep enbankment to the road. Then up he went, at a slow, easy angle. It took him a whole day.

All the people in the cars on that road were too busy to look down the bank. No one saw Hector toiling slowly up.

By the time he reached the top of the bank, night had come. There were not many cars on the road anymore. The smooth pavement under his feet gave his spirits a lift. He ran across the highway, his heavy tail swishing from side to side. Then he almost tumbled down the far bank.

The swamp beyond the road had been drained for pasture, but alongside it ran a drainage canal. The canal was deep enough for Hector to swim in, so he made his way lazily along it for several days. Something told him, though, that this was not the way home. So after a few days he hauled himself up the bank and pushed his way overland.

He was in a thicket now. Prickly bushes reached out with thorny arms. Ferns rose up in curling clumps. Tall reeds towered and toppled in a thick tangle. None of them could stop Hector. His handsome leathery coat was too tough to be harmed. His stocky legs were too strong to be stopped, except when he needed rest.

Hector did not have to hurry. He stopped for hours at a time to lie as still as a dead tree trunk. But one day he felt so discouraged about his long journey that he was almost ready to give it up.

There were plenty of creatures living in the thicket so that he was not lonely or hungry. There were snakes big and small. Raccoons lived in the hollows of trees, and birds called from their branches.

"Maybe I should just stay here," Hector thought gloomily, as he lay half asleep. He kept his eyes open a narrow slit, though, in case something good to eat happened by. That was how he noticed the catfish.

At first he could not believe his eyes. A fish on dry land? Surely that could not be. But it was. The big catfish was pushing itself along with its flippers, the spines on its nose waving as it went.

"Well," said Hector, "what are you doing here?"

"Just passing through," said the catfish. "My whiskers tell me that there is a swamp or canal not far ahead here, with plenty of good fish to eat. That's the place for me. What are you doing here?"

"I was on my way home," said Hector. "I wanted to get back to my home pond, but I've been traveling so long that I've about given up."

"Nonsense," said the catfish with a toss of its head. "An alligator doesn't belong on dry land any more than a catfish. At least not far from water. Think of the delicious wet green smell of the swamp, and of all those delightful little fishes and shrimps."

Hector thought of the swamp. And along with the shrimps and fishes and baby turtles he thought of bread and meat and marshmallows. So he raised himself up off his tummy and followed the walking catfish through the thicket.

Sure enough, Hector and his friend soon came to swamp again. The catfish plunged in with a splash. He was at his journey's end. But not Hector.

Fortunately for Hector, though, this swamp stretched all the hundred miles and more to his old home.

A road ran through part of the swamp. Hector was ambling across it when a truck driver spotted him. The driver stopped his truck with a screech of brakes. He hopped down, armed with a big club. Alligator skins bring a good price, and the truck driver wanted Hector's skin!

Hector opened his long jaws in a wide, tooth-filled grin, as a greeting to the man.

That was enough for the truck driver! He hopped back into his truck, started the motor, and drove swiftly away.

A mile or two down the road he stopped for coffee. "Saw an alligator on the road back a ways," he told his friends. "Big fellow. Must have been twelve feet long!"

"Oh, come on," his friends laughed. "Just walking down the road? Are you sure it wasn't a pink elephant?"

Most of the time, though, Hector didn't see any people. He met only other dwellers in the swamp. One day a crowd of pink flamingos flew in at sunset. They were just black shapes against the bright sky, with their long legs trailing behind them as they flew. But next morning, as they waded in the shallows, Hector could see that they were as brightly colored as tropical flowers.

The flamingos were busy, dipping their long necks to scoop out small snails from the mud with their specially-shaped beaks. They did not pay any attention to Hector. If Hector had not been so full of fish at the time, he might have snapped one up, long legs, bright feathers and all. But he only looked at them through half-closed eyes.

As Hector watched the flamingos stalk about, he heard a splash behind them. Young otters were sliding down the mud bank not far away. When they landed, they swam a few graceful yards, then bounded up the bank to slide down again. Hector did not move in their direction. Even if he had been very hungry, he knew those sleek otters were too fast for him.

So the weeks drifted by. Hector took his time. He lay in the shallows and let warm raindrops bounce on the water around him. He lay in the sun and let the life of the swamp world buzz and hum on every side. When he felt hungry he lashed his club of a tail at a passerby, or snapped his huge jaw,

and got himself a meal. But somewhere in the back of his slow, easy-going mind he still held the memory of his friend the man—and of those marshmallows!

So on he moved.

The weeks drifted into months. Back at Hector's old home pond, a few more houses had been built. It was called a lake now. Hector's friend still went fishing early in the mornings from his wooden pier. And once in a while he thought of Hector.

One morning the man had slept a little late. He was sitting at the breakfast table when he heard a bellow from the lake. There were lots of noises around the lake these days. But this one was different. There was something familiar about it, too.

There it came again—"Row-AH-H-rhh!"

"That surely sounds like Old Hector," said the man to his wife. So he pushed back his chair and went outside to see what he could see. As he stepped up onto the pier, there came Hector, swimming across the lake with waves streaming back from both sides of his jaw.

Hector thrashed his tail at the sight of his

99

old friend. When he came near the pier he reared up out of the water and grinned the full length of his long, curving jaw.

"Just a minute, Hector!" said his friend. He ran across the lawn to the house and was back in a minute with a large chunk of bread spread with dogfood. He tossed the bread, and Hector snapped it up in a flash.

In the old days, when Hector had had his snack he would settle down under the pier for a nap. But today he did not make a move. Instead he opened his jaws wide and let out another roar.

"Now what's the matter, Old Fellow?" his friend asked. He got another piece of bread spread with meat. Hector snapped it up, too. But then he gave another roar.

By now the man's wife was out of the house, too. So were neighbors all around the lake.

"I don't know what it is Old Hector wants," the man said to his wife.

"Marshmallows," said his wife. "You used to feed him marshmallows from the big old wooden spoon. It has his teeth marks on it to this day."

"Say, I'll bet that's it," laughed the man. So he ran to the house and found a handful of marshmallows and the old, tooth-marked wooden spoon. Back he came running, puffing a little.

Hector was waiting as patiently as he could. But when he saw those beautiful white marshmallows heaped up on the wooden spoon, he almost jumped clear out of the lake!

Hector snapped up the marshmallows. Then with a flick of his big tail he pushed himself under the wooden pier. And he settled down for a nice long nap. Hector Alligator was back home.

Note: Hector the Alligator really did make a 140-mile journey through the swamps and thickets of the Everglades back to his old home. He really had been trucked away to a state park by the Game and Fish Commission. He really did appear for his breakfast of bread and dogmeat, followed by marshmallows, at the home of his old friend after a long two years.

Now it's up to Hector to get along with the neighbors. If he behaves, and other people on the lake do not complain, he can stay, the men of the Game and Fish Commission say. Do you think Hector will understand?

P.S. There really are walking catfish, too, that travel overland between canals and swamps.

News for Blue Heron

WHEN THE BIRDS saw Blue Heron winging his way home at twilight, they all gathered to hear his news.

It was easy for the birds to find their way to Blue Heron's home. And there was plenty of room for them to perch on branches near his big messy old nest of sticks. For home to Blue Heron was in the upper branches of a tall eucalyptus tree that stood straight and tall and slim, waving its top like a fan against the sky.

There the birds gathered. There were small, rosy-headed finches, plump juncoes, mockingbirds, brown flickers. Even the busy, sharp-beaked woodpeckers stopped work sometimes to listen. And small hummingbirds hovered in midair, their wings whizzing so rapidly that they set up a small buzz.

Blue Heron was the largest of them all. When he flapped his great wide wings, he was impressive indeed. And he kept in touch with what went on all around the countryside.

Blue Heron was no stay-at-home. With his long legs streaming out behind him and his long neck tucked into an s-curve, he flew many miles each day. From his nest in the eucalyptus grove he circled up toward the green, rocky mountains. Then he headed out

101

over the sea. When he had had his morning's exercise, he settled down in the marsh, or slough as it was called, close to the coast. That slough was very important to him.

Several streams flowed down from the mountains. As they made their way across the flat land toward the sea they moved slowly, looping along in great curves. When there were rains in the mountains, those streams spread out over the flats to form wide, shallow ponds. Between rains, some of the water soaked in and some ran away to sea. But the whole area stayed watery enough to make an excellent home for turtles, thumb-sized green tree frogs by the thousands, toads, and other water creatures. They in turn made this a fine hunting ground for Blue Heron and his friends.

Brown Bittern and his mate made their homes in the slough. Various families of ducks and geese passing through stopped off for a pleasant, relaxing few days. And they always brought news. Blue Heron passed it on to the other birds when they gathered at twilight in the eucalyptus grove.

One evening Blue Heron had a worrisome report to make.

"The bitterns have a clutch of eggs in their nest," he began. That was good news. But there was more to come. "There were men in the slough today. They had big machines. Bittern is afraid they will disturb Mrs. Bittern so much that her eggs will not hatch. The machines also rattle the nests of the swallows who have built underneath the bridge that crosses the slough. I worry about them, too. And what will become of all the frogs and fish and other slough creatures if those noisy machines go roaring around?"

"Tell them what you think, Blue Heron," squawked noisy Jay.

So next day Blue Heron, with his long neck tucked into a curve and his long legs

102

streaming out behind him, flapped his way out to the slough. The men and their machines were still there. The men were calling and shouting to one another and the machines were roaring. The noise upset Mrs. Bittern and all the swallows so that they could scarcely stay on their nests to keep their eggs warm.

Blue Heron slanted his wings and swooped down close above the men's heads. Then he called, "Frawnk, frawnk, frawnk!" in a voice no one could miss.

The men stopped shouting. The machines stopped roaring. But as soon as Blue Heron beat his wings and sailed upward again, one of the men called out an order. The machines roared in reply. It was all just as noisy as before.

"Frawnk, frawnk!" croaked Blue Heron, beating the air with his wings.

In an office building nearby, a young woman ran to the window. She watched Blue Heron flapping his wings. She heard his anxious cry.

"What's the matter with that bird, Jodi?" a friend asked the young woman.

"He's upset because of those men with bulldozers down at the slough," she said. "And I don't blame him. Do you know what they are planning to do? They're going to drain that slough and dry it up. They will ruin the whole area if they have their way."

"Why don't you tell them what you think, Jodi?" said her friend.

So next day Jodi went to a meeting of the Planning Committee. She told them about the blue heron and the brown bitterns and the green tree frogs no bigger than a man's thumb, about the ring-necked snakes and all the other creatures of the slough that would be left without food or homes if the bulldozers had their way.

"Oh, no!" groaned the men.

"Well, it isn't hopeless," Jodi said. And she told them what they should do.

The following day, when Blue Heron flew over the slough, the men and machines were still there. But there was no shouting. The men were listening to Jodi, who was splashing through the slough in rubber boots.

"Bring it over here!" she called to the man who drove the biggest bulldozer.

Gently the bulldozer dipped its scoop into the swamp and lifted a huge hunk of dripping wet mud so carefully that the small green tree frogs taking mud baths scarcely knew that they were being moved.

Then the big scoop set that section of swamp down not far away, where Jodi had determined that it would be safe.

As Blue Heron watched, she guided the rescue of hundreds and hundreds of frogs. The man who ran the bulldozer hopped down once to rescue a ring-tailed snake. And Jodi stopped the trucks from rumbling across the bridge where the swallows had nested. She showed them a longer road around, and they politely went that way.

That evening back at the eucalyptus grove, Blue Heron's report was cheerful. "Brown Bittern says all the eggs have hatched, and the men are being careful to stay away from the nest. Bittern is sure that they will be able to raise their young. And the green tree frogs are doing very well in their new home."

"Good for Blue Heron!" squawked Jay.

All the birds joined in with chirps and calls. They were proud of Blue Heron for his part in helping the slough dwellers.

Next morning Blue Heron started off as usual in the direction of the rocky mountains. It had been a dry summer. The streams that flowed down the mountain slopes had vanished. The brush that grew among the rocks was very dry.

As Blue Heron floated above the mountain slopes, with his long neck tucked into an s-curve and his long thin legs streaming out behind, he saw two boys playing beside a mountain trail below. They were playing with matches!

One boy burned his finger on a match flame. With a cry, he threw the match away. It landed in dry grass. Soon a line of red and yellow flame spread out from the spot like a ripple on a pond. It reached a bush whose leaves were crisp and dry. They flamed up, and soon bushes on the mountain slope all around were aflame. The boys raced away down the trail.

Blue Heron knew what a forest fire could do. He flew low along the nearest road until he saw a car. Down he sailed over the car, calling his loudest, *"Frawnk, frawnk, frawnk!"*

The men in the car stopped to poke their heads out and look up at him. Then Blue Heron flew over the fire nearby, still croaking excitedly.

By now smoke was rising in a gray cloud stained with red. The men took shovels from the back of their car and raced up the trail toward the burning brush.

Luckily, the air was still. The men stamped and shoveled and packed dirt and leaves onto the fire to shut off the air supply. Soon they had it out. They got water and wet down the whole area. Then they drove along the trail until they found those two boys. They took the boys by their collars and led them roughly back to the car.

When the men drove away, Blue Heron checked the fire spot once more. The men had done a good job there. So he flew away for lunch at the slough.

"Lucky for the people that you were there," said pert Mrs. Junco when Blue Heron told his friends the news that night.

"It's lucky for everyone when Blue Heron is here," said Mrs. Oriole.

There were some things Blue Heron could not do much about. He could not stop a storm from blowing in from sea. But he could warn his friends when one was coming. He could tell them when rain clouds were settling down on the peaks, or when hot winds were about to blow through the

passes from the desert beyond the mountains. Then the birds could be prepared.

One day as he fished in the slough, wading long-legged among the reeds, Blue Heron met some seagulls. They had flown in from the islands out beyond the breakers. Many sea birds nested there on the rocks. Today the news from the islands was bad.

"Our mates are having a hard time," said one of the gulls. "So many of their eggs are breaking before they hatch."

"It isn't as bad as the time when the water was covered with thick black oil. Then anyone who dove for a fish was coated in heavy blackness. He could not fly again, try as he might. That was an awful thing to see," croaked a big gray gull, snapping with his red beak at a small fish. "This is not as bad as the oil, but it is a worry."

"You gulls are not having as bad a time as we pelicans," said a big brown fellow whose voice was a low, sad croak. "Where we nest out on the islands, you won't hear the squeak of a single fledgling pelican this season. All the eggs shattered in the nests."

"What happened?" Blue Heron asked.

"No one knows," was the reply. Brown Pelican was looking out to sea where a line of his fellow pelicans skimmed along close to the water. *Flap, flap, sail,* they went, *flap, flap, coast,* in perfect rhythm. "The shells are just too thin," Brown Pelican went on. "When the mother birds sit on the nests, the egg shells break under them."

The birds did not know it, but men were worried about the lack of baby pelicans, too. They thought it was the fault of factories near the shore. The factory wastes carried chemicals into the sea water. Small fish and shellfish swallowed those chemicals. They in turn were snapped up by birds, including the pelicans. The chemicals caused the pelican eggs to have very thin shells.

But it seemed the men could not stop the factories from spewing out wastes.

"Things are dangerous out at sea," said Mrs. Junco that night, when Blue Heron brought home news of his talk with Gray Gull and Brown Pelican.

"We are not all safe here on land either," rapped out Old Woodpecker. "Men are spraying poison on their trees. Whoever eats bugs or fruit where they have sprayed will die. I myself have seen many dead birds."

"And I," put in Mockingbird.

"Still, we are better off here, safe at home," said Mrs. Junco, who never traveled far.

All the birds agreed. So did Blue Heron.

He settled down that night in his scruffy old nest feeling very contented.

Every morning as usual Blue Heron flew away. He flew up the mountain slopes. He circled out to sea. After a visit with the bitterns and the swallows and the gulls, he was ready to start for home.

Soon the bitterns were about to leave for the winter with their little brood. "The slough will be different next year," Mrs. Bittern said. "But thanks to you, Blue Heron, I think the men will take care. We plan to come back again to raise our young here."

"I am glad," said Blue Heron. Then he flew back to the eucalyptus grove.

When he neared his home, he thought his eyes must have deserted him. The tall fans of the eucalyptus trees were nowhere to be seen, standing straight and slender against the sky. Blue Heron circled the spot where they had been, calling as he flew. Now he could see what was left of the trees lying flat on the ground. The sticks of his big, messy nest were scattered far and wide.

"Frawnk! Frawnk! Frawnk!" Blue Heron cawed in distress.

Out from the liveoaks and the sycamores came the juncoes and mockingbirds and woodpeckers and jays. Out came the orioles and rosy-headed finches, chirping and calling in sympathy.

Blue Heron settled down on the ground near the stump of his tall eucalyptus tree. The smaller birds all gathered around.

"Men came!" cried Mrs. Junco.

"With machines!" squawked Jay. "I went after them, you may be sure."

"I went after them too," screeched Mockingbird. "I dove at them. I tried to peck at their heads. But without you, what could we do?"

"They are going to build houses," said Woodpecker. "No doubt they will cut down the liveoaks and sycamores too. I will have nowhere to hunt bugs."

"And where will we make our homes?" chirped sad little rosy-headed Finch.

"The world is changing," said Blue Heron, standing straight and tall. "There are fires on the mountains and machines in the swamps. Eggs shatter out at sea, poison covers the trees, and black oil fouls the seabirds' wings. I think People are to blame.

"Some are trying to help, but it is not enough. There are too many people. I am growing old. I must find a place with quiet and peace and no people around. Goodbye, my friends."

106

Then Blue Heron flew off into the twilight, with his long neck tucked into an s-curve, and his thin legs streaming out behind.

The small birds sadly watched him go. Back at their nests they talked things over. Some decided to leave. Others decided that the next year they would find a new nesting place. A few decided to stay.

Now at twilight those who are left gather wherever they can. But no Blue Heron comes flying in with news of all the countryside. Not many chirps and twitters and songs are heard.

"The world is changing," the small birds say sadly. "Nothing is as pleasant as it was."

They still build nests where they can. They lay eggs and hunt bugs and teach their babies to fly.

"This is the only world we have," they say. "We must do our best with it." And they chirp as merrily as they are able.

At twilight the breeze still stirs the leaves on the trees that remain. Then the birds think of the eucalyptus grove standing tall against the sky. They remember Blue Heron and his vanished home, and they sigh for the good old days.

Note: There really was a blue heron who lost his home a hundred feet above the ground in a eucalyptus tree just last spring. He did fly each day to a nearby slough for lunch. And there is a young woman named Jodi who helped save the creatures of that slough from men and their machines.

She and other people like her are trying hard to keep some spots in the world safe for the birds and beasts. But all the troubles Blue Heron saw and felt and heard about are real. It will take more men and women, and many, many boys and girls, all working together, to make sure that the world is safe for all kinds of living things.

At the Pond

Brown Deer comes to the pond to drink.
What does he see there? What do you think?
Out of the water hops a green frog.
Two painted turtles doze on a log.
Three beavers sit on their mud-roofed house.
He sees four ducks swimming, five plump grouse.
Out of the woods march six striped skunks.
Five squirrels chatter from the oak tree's trunk,
Four woodpeckers go "Rat-a-tat-tat."
Three owls hoot, and Deer thinks, "That is that."
Then two mice whisper something into his ear,
And, looking in the water, he sees one Brown Deer!

Sea and Shore

If you look out over the sea—any sea—from the shore, you cannot get a glimpse of land on the far side.

A sea or ocean is a very large body of water. In fact, the seas and oceans flow together to cover most of the surface of the earth, much more than all the land put together. Where blocks of rocky earth push up above the level of the seas, we call the edges of the land coasts or shores.

The water in the oceans all around the world is always in motion. There are even streams of water that flow like rivers through the oceans; we call them currents.

The surface of the water is stirred by the breezes or winds moving in the air above. But the oceans and seas move in another way that is even stranger than this. As the moon circles the earth, millions of miles away, it pulls the waters of earth toward it

slightly. We call the rising of the waters toward the moon high tide.

All this water moving constantly against the rocks along the shores has worn a great deal of rock down into fine grains called sand. That is why in some places we have sandy beaches. At other places there are small stones, or pebbles, on the beach instead of sand. In some places the land drops off sharply at the edge of the water, and there is no beach at all.

There are many creatures that live along the shore, both on the land side and in the water. In the water live fish and many other sea creatures. Some have shells on the outside instead of bones inside; we call them shellfish. Others look more like plants than animals; some of these are sea anemones, sea cucumbers, and coral. There are also many real plants that grow in the waters.

Some creatures live both on land and in the sea. Seals and walruses are animals that live most of their lives in the water but come ashore to have their babies and spend some time out of the water, sitting on rocks. Sea turtles also live most of their lives in the water but crawl up on sandy beaches to lay their eggs in scooped-out hollows.

Many birds are as much at home on the water as on land. They seldom travel inland out of sight of the sea. Some make their nests on rocky cliffs, others in protected spots close to the water. They catch their food by snatching fish from the sea or by hunting for tiny creatures on the sands of the beaches. If you look closely at the sands, you will see some of these small creatures—little crabs scuttling sideways, black beetles and others. You may see very small bubbly holes in the sand that mark some small creature's hiding place.

There are also many people who like to live near the sea. Some of them spend much of their time on the water, steaming along in big ships that carry goods and people to faraway lands. Others brave the often stormy seas in smaller ships and boats to catch fish for a living.

Still other people come to the shore for holidays. They like the sound of the surf, the feel of the sand under bare feet, the salty smell of the sea air. Some like to fish or go boating or build sand castles. Others just lie on the sun-baked sand and think long, slow, sleepy thoughts. Which do you think you would rather do, if you were beside the sea?

Whales on the Beach

"LET'S PLAY Follow the Leader," called Adolfo Dolphin. He gave a saucy flip of his tail. It was meant to show that if he were the leader everyone would have fun.

"Good idea! Let's!" cried a dozen voices. So they all fell in line, more than fifty sleek dolphins with their dorsal fins curling back jauntily.

They were ready for a new game. It was a fine day at sea. The water was warm. The early sunshine twinkled from its surface. A light breeze rippled over the sea.

The dolphins had been sporting close to the shoreline for hours. They had swum races and played games of tag. They had had competitions to see who could leap highest out of the water to sail through the air in a graceful curve.

For a while they had been bubbling with joy. They they began to feel bored. They wanted a new game.

"What shall we do now?" they called to one another. Their clear tones rang out over the water as they spoke in sounds men are still trying to learn to understand.

It was then that Adolfo suggested Follow the Leader. What a chase he led them! They raced along the shoreline, leaping and flipping their sleek round bodies in smooth side rolls. They swung into the wide mouths of rivers that wound through swamps to the sea. Then, flipping their tails to turn themselves, the line swung out toward deep water again.

Finally even the leader was beginning to tire. He led his long file more slowly along the shore of a shallow gulf. Then he nosed into the breakers that rose and foamed softly into the yellow sand.

"Hey!" called a young dolphin named Dan. "My flippers touch sand. We're getting in too close."

"Are you afraid to follow?" Adolfo sneered. He flipped his tail a little, just enough to move him even closer to shore.

"This is too much!" thought some of the dolphins. But no one wanted to be the first to leave the line. So they flipped their tails a little and nosed in shoreward too.

All but Dan Dolphin. "I quit!" he cried. "This is dumb." He flipped his tail the other way and swam out through the breakers into deeper water.

Before anyone could follow him, a gray cloud came scudding in from the sea. A squally wind stirred up the breakers. Waves and dolphins were pushed in toward the sand.

"Help! I'm stuck!" cried one dolphin after another. And they were.

Adolfo Dolphin did not say anything. He was thrashing wildly, churning up sand. But he was stranded in just one foot of water. So were those in line behind him. And the squally wind was blowing more and more of them inshore.

The young dolphins were frightened. Like bigger whales, they needed to feel water on their skins to be comfortable. If they were out of water with the sun shining on them for long, they would be sick. If they did not get free soon, they might die.

They waved their flippers and wriggled their tails. Sand and water flew through the air. But the dolphins could not swim free.

On the sand, a boy named Don was having his morning run. He was jogging down the beach to meet his friend Bob. As he jogged, Don heard a commotion out at sea.

He saw the dolphins in trouble near the line of breakers.

"Look!" Don called to Bob. He waved an arm toward the sea. "Dolphins! I think they're aground."

Bob shaded his eyes to look into the morning sun.

"You're right," he cried. "They need help. Let's get the others."

Bob raced down the beach and Don raced back up. They called to all the boys and girls, and out they came, ready for fun.

"Rescue needed!" called Bob and Don. "Dolphins aground."

"What do we do?" asked some of the boys.

"Hop aboard and steer them out," cried a small brown girl named Sue. She ran into the surf, lifting her feet high.

When she came to the first dolphin, Sue gave it a push, as if it had been a canoe. Adolfo Dolphin, for it was he, did not understand. He batted Sue with his tail.

112

Down went Sue, her legs flying. Adolfo hadn't really meant to do that. But Sue didn't mind. She bounced up with a laugh, spitting out sea water. Then she tugged at Adolfo's flipper to turn him seaward. And she hopped on his back, flinging one brown leg across him. Kicking him gently in the sides with her heels, Sue spoke into what she hoped was his ear. (The ears of dolphins and other whales are very hard to see.)

"Let's go!" said Sue. At the strange sound Adolfo pushed with everything he had! Sand spurted up behind him. He was afloat!

Sue rode Adolfo out until the water was clear and deep below. She clung with both hands to his smooth back, and he did not try any of his fancy rolls.

When they reached deep water, Sue slid off. "Keep going!" she called. And she gave Adolfo a friendly farewell slap.

He flipped his tail in a happy wave, but Sue was already swimming back toward shore.

On the way back, she met a crowd of dolphins and riders. One boy waved a hand in greeting. As he did, his dolphin gave a spurt and the boy slid off. For a moment only his feet showed, kicking above the waves. Sputtering and blowing, he joined Sue on the short swim back toward the beach to pick up new mounts.

Now a boat came putt-putting along. It belonged to the Marine Patrol. The crew of the boat shook their heads and laughed as they saw the dolphins being ridden out to safety, guided with friendly heels and hands and knees.

Before long all the dolphins were safe in deep water.

Now the beach was lined with people. All the proud parents had come down to see their dolphin-riding boys and girls. They clapped and called and came running with towels as the boys and girls came stumbling in through the surf when their work was done.

"Look!" cried someone. "Look out to sea!"

Up and down along the coast swam the troop of happy dolphins. They dove and spouted through their blow holes and stood on their tails. They leaped through the air as gracefully as ballet stars. And across the water the people could hear happy dolphin calls as the small whales gave their thank-you show.

Note: This troop of small whales really did ground themselves on a sandy beach not long ago. And boys and girls really did hop on their backs and ride them safely out to sea.

Whales of the smaller sizes usually do travel in large groups, following a leader. If the leader leads the group too close to the beach, they may all lose their lives, because their weight is so great that out of water it presses their lungs flat and they cannot breathe.

A Whale of a Thing

IF SOMEONE SAYS, "That's a whale of a thing," he means it is very, *very* big. Some whales grow to be more than a hundred feet long. These blue whales are the biggest living creatures in the world. Some of their smallest cousins, porpoises and dolphins, may be only about five feet long when they are fully grown, though most of them range between fourteen and thirty feet.

Whales are sea animals, shaped much like fish. They are not fish, though. They have to go up to the surface to breathe air, and they give birth to baby whales instead of laying eggs as fish do.

Baby whales are loved and cared for tenderly by their mothers. They drink mother's milk when they are small and like to snuggle up to their mothers.

Whales call out and signal to one another in squeals or squeaks, whines or booms like sad bagpipes.

Some of the largest have no teeth; instead, they have strainers in their mouths to sort their food. Their throats are so small that they cannot swallow anything that is more than two inches long. They are called baleen whales from the word for their bony strainers, which were once used in making ladies' corsets! Baleen whales feed on tiny shellfish and other sea creatures. They eat millions at a time, as much as a ton at a meal. Remember that the blue whale, largest of the baleens, is as big as twenty-five elephants!

Many of these whales plow along the ocean floor, scooping in whatever they find. When their baleen strainers have sorted the food, they may stand up on their tails to swallow it more easily.

Some of the smaller whales do their hunting for food at the surface instead of on the sea bottom. They are fierce hunters and meat eaters. They have rows of sharp teeth and will attack much bigger creatures than they are, including giant whales and bulky walruses. They slash their prey so fiercely that they are known as killer whales.

Many of the giant whales prefer to travel by themselves, but the killers swim in noisy packs, and dolphins and pygmies, like those in the story "Whales on the Beach," like to travel in large groups. Sometimes they make expeditions up rivers and into shallow bays. Groups of them sometimes swim into shore and find themselves trapped. No one knows why.

114

One Bird Lost

"WH-R-R-R! WH-R-R-R!" the plover whistled. He waited, then whistled again. There was no reply. Far below him he could hear the slosh and heave of the waves as they tossed up foam. But Young Plover could not see the waves below. Around him swirled a thick, wet cloud. The cloud that hid the sea below had also separated him from the other birds in his flight.

"Wh-r-r-r!" he whistled once more, hoping to hear an answering call. None came.

Young Plover had never dreamed of traveling alone over the wide sea. He had never made this journey before. He had been born only that summer, hatched from an egg in a mossy nest near an arctic beach. There his mother had fed him on insect mash until he was old enough to hunt his own food.

Then he found plenty of insects buzzing around the low arctic plants. And he found the berries that ripened on the bushes as tasty as insects, or even better. He ate and ate. As he ate he grew big—eleven inches long by Man's measure—and strong and plump.

He would soon need all the strength he could store, for he and his fellows had one of the longest of all bird migrations ahead.

It would be a long journey even for humans traveling by airplane. The young plovers would fly from the arctic coast of Alaska to the rocky coast of Argentina, close to the Antarctic. There they would enjoy another summer of pale, clear, endless days.

Young Plover did not know that. He only knew that he had been getting more and more restless. After feasting for weeks on bugs and berries, he did not care to eat anymore at all. He did not care to run along at the edge of the waves, feeling the water nip at his thin toes and long legs. All he wanted to do was fly.

Soon it was time for the birds to leave. Other flocks had been gathering on the beach around them, and whirling off into the southern skies. Something inside told

them that winter was coming and that they should find a land with another summer, with more bugs and berries and sun.

The grown-up plovers had been an early group to leave. The youngsters were not experienced enough in flying to leave then. But at last their turn came too. Young Plover left with a large flock of youngsters. They started confidently toward the south, over the sea. When the clouds overtook them, and storm winds tossed them, snow began to weigh down their oiled feathers. Most of the flock turned toward land.

Young Plover, tossed on the strange wind, somehow did not hear their signals. He did not see them turn. He struggled on, not knowing for some time that he was alone.

When he realized what had happened, he tried to find the other birds. He beat his wings faster to push himself up, up. But the flock was not flying above him. Then down, down he coasted through the cloud. But he found no plovers. Even if they had been there, they could not have heard his whistle over the roar of wind and waves.

Deep inside him the plover still knew which way he should be going. Something pulled him toward the south, though all his world was blanketed in clouds. He veered a little to the west. No plovers there. A little to the east he went. No plovers there.

He was alone and unhappy about it. But there seemed nothing to do but fly on to the south. So on he went.

Flying was not easy now. His wings were becoming heavy with snow that froze to a coating of ice. He tried to beat his wings faster against the air, but his sturdy muscles were tiring fast.

Closer and closer to the waves he dropped. Their caps of icy foam seemed to be tossed straight at him. If they caught him, he would be lost.

116

Then something dark appeared on the waves below. It was a fishing boat, lost in the storm. With a last weary push Young Plover pointed himself toward it. Soon he fluttered down with outspread wings onto the small Eskimo canoe.

"A bird!" cried one of the fishermen. He pulled off a glove and put his warm hand gently around the bird. Then he tucked it under his jacket until the icy coating melted from its wings, and its small pounding heart steadied its rapid beat.

For hours the boat tossed in the storm. Then gradually the wind blew the clouds into long threads that sailed away, leaving the sky cold and clear.

"Which way is the shore?" the youngest fisherman asked. He had never been at sea in weather like this. He did not like it much.

"The bird will tell us," an older man said. "He will know which way is south. That's the way he wants to go. We can get our directions from him."

The young fisherman opened his jacket. The plover gripped the boy's sleeve with his curling toes and turned his thin beak into the wind. He moved his wings, slowly at first. His muscles felt strong again. His feathers felt light and dry. He beat the air more strongly with his wings. And with a piping cry, up he flew!

During the storm he had floundered through the air. But now he did not hesitate. Something inside him steered him straight on the course he should take. His beak was pointed toward the south where he had never been.

The fishermen sat with paddles poised as Young Plover soared away with strong wingbeats. Then, setting their course by his mysterious built-in compass, they headed confidently for home. Young Plover had showed them the way.

A Treat for Young Sea Otter

"PLAYTIME, playtime!" called Young Sea Otter, when he and his mother finished their dinner.

Dinner had been a chewy, delicious abalone that Mrs. Otter brought up from the sea bottom. The abalone had been tightly fastened to its rock. Mrs. Otter had to dive over and over again to loosen it.

Young Sea Otter did not like being left floating by himself. He liked to have his mother close by. He whimpered and cried a little while his mother was at work. But at last Mrs. Otter was back from her hunt, tightly clutching the big abalone shell and blowing water out of her whiskers.

If it had been a hard-shelled king crab she had found, she would have made one more dive for a good round stone. With the stone for a tool and the crab shell on her chest, she would have cracked it open with loud, sharp blows. For Mrs. Otter was rare among animals in knowing how to use tools.

She did not need a rock to crack the abalone, though. She lay on her back on the green and purple sea with the abalone shell on her chest and fed bits of the meat to Young Otter who played about at her side.

Soon they both felt happy and well fed—for the time being. An otter has to eat about a quarter of its weight in food every day, so the abalone would not be their last meal of the afternoon.

"Playtime!" Young Otter reminded his mother.

"So it is," said Mrs. Otter. "What would you like to do?"

She fondled her youngster with her long flippers, and bumped noses with him in an otter kiss. Then she stroked her flipper paws gently through his fur to squeeze out water from among the inner hairs. This helps keep sea otters warm. Mrs. Otter groomed her own fur in the same way.

"Let's go to the rocks near the shore," said Young Otter. "The seal pups say it is fun to watch the people's children play."

Mrs. Otter hesitated. She worried about Young Otter, and she did not feel safe too near the shore. Two years before, she had had another baby. He had swum in toward shore by himself one day as she hunted for food on the sea-bottom rocks. When she

117

baby still was not clean. She wrapped him in kelp and rubbed him well. Some of the oil came off at last, but with it went the special insulation that keeps seals' and otters' fur from becoming waterlogged.

Baby Otter soon caught a chill, and for all his mother's tender care, he died.

Now Mrs. Otter was anxious to keep her new son safe and sound. But if the seals were on the rocks with their pups, it must be safe to go there, she decided.

"All right," she said.

She swam through the kelp bed, in toward shore, with Young Otter paddling at her side. The thicket of seaweed called kelp, with its long curving stems and thick leaves, was really their home. Mrs. Otter felt safest in the kelp, but now she left it behind.

The seal family was there when the otters reached the rocks. The young pups were squealing at their play. They liked to let the waves carry them up almost to the top of the rocks. Then the waves would break and sink down with a sloshing sound. The young seals would slide along the rocks on their shiny and slippery fronts.

"May I play with them?" Young Otter begged.

"You had better stay in the water," his mother said. Young Otter looked so disappointed that she added, "We can go up onto the lowest rocks to get a better view."

From the first line of wet rocks, the seals and otters had a good view of the shore. The most fun was to watch the children at play on the beach. Those golden-brown, fuzzy-topped children, with their funny long arms and legs (so the seals and otters thought) ran along the sand or fell on their fronts in the blue-green water spangled with white foam close to the seashore.

"There are more than ever today," cried the little seals. "And such happy ones! See

came up and called for him, a sad cry answered her.

Her baby had swum into a pool of black oil floating on the sea. His fur was weighted down with thick, sticky black goo.

Mrs. Otter had done everything she could. She dove with him into deep water. But the oil did not flow from his fur as sand would have done. She stroked and groomed him with her flippers. Soon her flippers were gummy with the heavy oil, but the

118

the round little one playing with the big toy? And the funny little fellow in the bright red trunks, running down the sand!"

"See them laughing and talking with each other," said Young Otter. "I wonder what they say."

What do you suppose those children were saying? Do you think they said, "Oh, see the seals! And I think I see an otter, too. There are more than ever today, and such happy ones! See them flop on the rocks and swim out in the sea with just their shiny black faces bobbing above the waves."

Maybe that is what the children said. Young Otter and the seal pups could not tell. But they stayed for a long time on the rocks. The children stayed on the beach. They watched each other and they laughed for joy, children, seals and otter alike.

When the sun was sinking and a cool breeze drifted in from the open sea, the people mothers rubbed their children with big towels and wrapped them in sweaters and took them away.

Out on the rocks, Mrs. Sea Otter said, "It is time for us to go too."

So Young Otter said goodbye to the seal pups and swam off with his mother, back to their home in the forest of kelp. He dove with his mother for the spiny sea urchins that are bread and meat to sea otters.

The sea urchins live by nibbling kelp. If the otters did not eat a lot of urchins in turn, the beds of seaweed in which they make their homes might entirely disappear.

By the time the sea otters had finished off their meal of sea urchins, the last rosy light of day was sinking into the western sea.

Mrs. Otter put her child to bed, wrapping him in a blanket of kelp. The long strands of seaweed would keep him from drifting ashore as he slept.

Then Mrs. Sea Otter lay on her back close by. She poked out her feet in a long, delicious stretch. Next she pulled a blanket of kelp across herself, strand by nice slimy strand. She laid her paws on her chest, as Young Otter had done.

Soon mother and child both were fast asleep, rocked by the gentle waves. Perhaps Young Otter dreamed in the night of the children he had seen that day.

Jungle and Rain Forest

FLY OVER a rain forest and, looking down, you see below just a rough, bumpy-looking carpet of green. What you see are the leafy tops of trees known as forest giants that tower high above the ground.

Paddle or chug through the rain forest in a small river boat and, looking up, you can scarcely see a sliver of blue sky. You cannot even catch a glimpse of the leafy tops of those forest giants through the tangle of bushes, trees and twisting vines.

Peer off into the dim, deep greenery and you will have the feeling that only plants live in the rain forest. You may hear some birds calling to one another, or see a flash of bright feathers, but you will probably not see another animal, not even a curious monkey swinging through the trees. This is because most of the animals stay hidden from sight during the day.

Travel through the dripping rain forest on foot, and you will find the going really hard. You will need a sturdy knife to chop away tough stalks and branches. Stems and twigs

120

grow swiftly here, and it is difficult to keep trails open. You had better watch where you step, too. There are not many clear spots on the ground, and there are many snakes about.

When you make camp, you will need to spread netting over your sleeping bag, to keep out most of the insects. Some will probably nip at you no matter what care you take!

In the night you may hear shrieks and howls in the blackness. The brush will crackle near your camp as hunting animals push their way through.

There are really many dwellers in the forest, you will begin to realize. Night brings out the wild hunting cats—tigers in some forests, lions in others, ocelots, pumas, leopards, or jaguars. There are otters and raccoons, too, and other families related to some of the woods animals of cooler lands.

In the treetops live countless bright-feathered birds, and also numerous monkeys, many of them swinging through the trees by their long arms or tails. Down below live their larger cousins the baboons, chimpanzees and apes. There are lizards and anteaters and many creatures that seldom see the light of day.

True rain forests lie in low areas close to the equator, in some of the hottest lands on earth. Not many people live in them, and not many roads run through them, so they are rather hard to visit.

Not all wild places thickly overgrown with trees and brush are rain forests, though. Some wild woods may be rather dry but still so untamed that they are left to the wild animals. These forests are often called jungles. Where forest giants have been cut down and the lower brush has grown up in a thick tangle, it is often called "the bush."

There are even some wide grassy plains that are still left to wild animals. Ponds lie in the midst of them, and at dawn and dusk

many of the animals gather at these water holes to drink, each politely waiting its turn.

More roads and trails have been cut through bush country and grasslands than through rain forests. Some wide, smooth trails have been cleared and tramped down by marching herds of elephants. Since these usually run in quite straight lines between water holes, they are followed by many other animals. Even where there are no roads, it is possible to bounce over the bumpy land in a four-wheel-drive vehicle.

Zebras and antelopes of many kinds wander these grasslands in great herds. Giraffes stalk about on their long, stiff-jointed legs, nibbling at the tips of thorny trees. If they are startled or frightened, they may break into a strangely graceful, long-legged, floating kind of trot.

Elephants by the dozens march along trunk to tail, with the babies tucked between their mothers' front legs. Now and then they pause to tear at branches with their strong trunks, stripping off the tasty twigs and leaves. Or with creaks and groans and crashes they uproot a whole tree.

Lions, swift cheetahs and other members of the cat family move silently about hunting food for themselves and their young. They visit the water holes, too.

In the larger pools and streams, big, clumsy-looking hippopotamuses may wallow half underwater during the hot daylight hours. At night they waddle ashore to munch grasses with loud, chomping sounds.

A hippopotamus is not the only animal that looks clumsy to people. There is also the single-horned rhinoceros, who seems to be a leftover from the age of the dinosaurs.

Here and there people have tried to move into the jungle with herds of tame cattle and fields of tame plants. But large stretches of rain forest, jungle and grassland are still the kingdom of the free wild animals.

Tanto Elephant Grows Up

THERE WAS once a young elephant who lived in a jungle. His mother loved him very much, and she called him Tanto.

The jungle where Tanto and his mother lived with their herd was a wonderful place. Nearby were wide golden grasslands where huge herds of animals wandered. There were heavy-shouldered wildebeests that humped along stiffly like big wooden toys, their gray beards streaming in the wind. There were plump, striped zebras that raced away, if they were frightened, with a sound like the swift beat of many small drums. There were impala and other antelopes of many sizes and families, some with curved and some with twisty horns. Their coats were colored like the yellow grass and its dark shadows. Tanto knew them all.

At the edges of the grasslands grew silvery thorn trees, big bulging baobabs with small twigs for branches, and flat-topped acacia trees whose bare limbs rose and spread like the twisted spokes of a big umbrella the wind had blown inside out. In the heat of the day lions liked to lie stretched out on those branches, watching over their roly-poly cubs at play. Tanto knew them, too.

Tanto Elephant had learned to know all the places and creatures of his wild jungle. At nightfall, as he lay stretched out between his mother's legs just before he went to sleep, he liked to listen to the jungle sounds.

He could hear the twitter and call of birds in the tree branches, talking together as they settled down to rest. He knew the squawks and barks and squeals of the brown baboons as they settled for the night, each one in place around the proud granddaddy leader of the pack. He knew the hyena's sorrowful wail, the zebra's bark.

When Tanto had listened his fill to all the jungle voices, he let the lullaby of the breeze through the crisp forest leaves take over. Then he would nudge his mother gently, to make certain that she was really there, and, yawning a wide pink yawn behind his trunk, he would drift happily off to sleep.

On the morning of our story, Tanto awoke as usual, thirsty for some of his mother's good milk. But these days Tanto's mother kept

123

pushing him away. There was always a lady elephant nearby willing to see to it that Tanto was fed. These ladies were good friends of his mother's, and Tanto knew them as aunties. He liked them all, and they were good to him, but Tanto could not understand the change in his mother.

They had always been so close. Whether they marched with the herd in an orderly line or rambled through the brush with a few friends, Tanto always knew where his place was—under his mother's swaying trunk, between her strong front legs. There he felt safe, and now and then his mother would flip up her trunk's soft tip and feed him a tender leafy shoot.

But today, when Tanto tried to take his place behind her trunk, his mother pushed him away, as she had been doing lately. One of the aunties who had no youngster of her own soon ambled over with a leafy tidbit for Tanto. But he could not understand what had made his mother change.

"Let's go for a walk," suggested the auntie.

Tanto did not really want to go. He wanted to stay near his mother. But she kept pushing him away with her trunk, so Tanto followed the auntie down one of the elephant trails.

Tanto knew the trail. It led to a pleasant water hole. This was a place Tanto always liked to visit, especially at a time like this, in the cool of early morning. For the water hole was a popular place.

As Tanto and his auntie drew near, a pair of gray warthogs came trotting along, noses to the ground, their thin tails straight in the air. They dodged around the heavy, brown shoulders of some water buffalo, keeping out of reach of their wide, swaying horns. On the far shore of the water hole a herd of zebra were approaching. The early sun glinted on the changing pattern of their black and white stripes until they shimmered before Tanto's eyes. Behind them came impala, leaping across

the golden grasslands. And against the sky-line Tanto could see the towering necks of quiet, shy giraffes.

Tanto's mother had always found a place where he could wriggle through the crowd to the water for a drink. Animals were packed so thickly that each had to politely wait his or her turn. Tanto's mother was willing to wait politely, too. As she waited she would lick the good, salty rocks that added flavor to her diet of twigs and leaves. But she had always managed to get a drink for Tanto without delay. Today that too was changed.

Auntie said, "Wait, child. Wait your turn," when Tanto squealed and waved his trunk and wanted to push his way through. He fussed a little, because he did not understand, so Auntie thumped with one big foot on the soft ground. She thumped until she had made a sizable hole.

As Tanto peered into the hole, he saw water oozing up from the bottom. Soon there was enough to give him a drink. It was not the same as wading into the water hole, snorting and blowing and spraying a stream of cool water like a showerbath, Tanto thought sadly. He nibbled a twig or two, but the brown leaves on the bushes near this much-traveled spot were not as tasty as the juicy water weeds that grew in the middle of the

water hole. Tanto sighed softly to himself.

"Come along, child," said Auntie when they had both had a drink. She waited for Tanto to take the tip of her tail in his trunk. That was the way grown-up elephants marched in line. But Tanto was used to the comfort of walking under his mother's shadow. He tried to push around in front of Auntie, but she shoved him gently back. At last he took the grown-up position and sedately marched along.

A herd of graceful impala came toward them. The young were leaping lightly across the grass while the grown-ups strolled along. It was Tanto who noticed a rippling of grass stalks alongside the impala herd. It was Tanto who saw the lion's dark mane moving softly, smoothly, all unsuspected, toward the herd.

"Look, Auntie!" called Tanto, tweaking the lady elephant's tail.

Auntie looked around in surprise. It was strange for a lion to be hunting in broad daylight. When the sun is high in the sky, lions are usually asleep or resting quietly in the shade.

"It is not our affair," said Auntie. "Father Lion has a family to feed. Come along now."

Tanto curled the tip of his trunk around his auntie's tail and followed her down the path. But from the corner of his eye he could

see that the impala herd was on the alert now, the grown-ups pricking their ears and looking over their shoulders.

Tanto really enjoyed the rest of the day. He and Auntie watched some weaver birds shaping their neat round basket nest on the bare branch of a thorn tree. When Auntie complained of an itching shoulder, a small bird landed politely on her back and peck-pecked at her wrinkled leather coat until the itch was gone.

The best part of the day was the visit to the river that cut its way through the middle of the forest. It chuckled along between banks, one high and muddy, the other low and reedy. Tanto and his auntie reached the river on the side where the bank was high. They stood for a long moment looking down, watching a blue kingfisher diving for fish and a long-legged egret wading out with delicate, high-footed steps, hunting for plump frogs.

"Can't we go down?" Tanto begged.

"Yes," said Auntie. "You may go down the slide if you like." She waved her trunk at a smooth, wide track that cut through the steep bank at a slant.

Tanto knew that slide. He felt very grown up being allowed to lead the way down it. He headed for the mud slide at a run, his small trunk swinging for joy. At the top he flung out his front legs and, trumpeting with

glee, he flopped down on his plump tummy.

Slickery-slide, down he went, to land in the river with a delightful splash.

At the splash the blue kingfisher went flying. The egret looked up in surprise. Then down the slide came great big Auntie. *Slickery-slide-ker-SPLASH!* she landed. Even the egret flew away at that! And a tall crested crane from the meadow beyond tossed his proud head and spread his wide wings and, tucking up his long legs, flew away too.

"That was splendid!" cried Tanto, spraying trunkfuls of river water on all sides. "Let's do it again."

"No," said Auntie, puffing a little. "Enough is enough. We're here now, so enjoy yourself."

"I wish Mama were here too," said Tanto, mumbling a little around a dripping mouthful of tasty water weeds.

"Yes," said Auntie. And for a moment her kind face looked anxious. That was another thing Tanto did not understand.

When the frolic in the river was over, Tanto and his auntie marched across a sandbar to the farther shore. The sandbar was crisscrossed with rows of footprints—feathery star-shaped prints of birds, small deep stabs made by sharp antelope hoofs, big padded paw prints of lions and other cats. Tanto knew them all. His mother had taught him. He would have liked to show her how well he had learned his lesson. But his mother was not here.

On the way back to where they had left the herd, Tanto and his auntie paused in a shady thicket for some lunch. Tanto's mother had always done the ripping and tearing of the tree branches. Then she had chosen the most tender bits to give to him.

Now Auntie said, "There's a good branch, Tanto. Pull it off."

Tanto was surprised at how much fun it was to feel the branch bend and rip away—with a loud snap—and to know he had done it all by himself.

The puffy clouds sailing high above the thorn trees were pink with sunset light by the time the two neared their home area again. Tanto was sleepy after his long day. He wanted to tell his mother all about it.

As they came down the homeward trail, Tanto heard a rumbling of voices ahead. Soon he saw a group of his aunties, friends of his mother, standing in a circle. They were all looking down at something on the ground. One after another they showered puffs of sand on whatever it was. Tanto pushed his way through the circle for a better look.

There in the center stood his mother, looking tired. Beside her on the ground lay a small, damp, pale-gray, brand-new elephant baby. The lady elephants were blowing sand over it to dry its damp skin.

As Tanto watched silently, the baby scrambled unsteadily to its feet. Its small legs did not seem very strong, but its mother—Tanto's own mother—guided it with her trunk. When the baby took its first steps, it raised its small trunk toward one of the lady elephants, pleading for some milk.

"It doesn't even know its own mother," said Tanto in a whisper.

His mother looked at him and smiled. She stroked him gently with the tip of her trunk. "But my good big boy does," she said.

Then, trumpeting softly, she lifted the baby in her trunk and brought it back to the middle of the circle. She knelt and, resting her head on the ground, gave the baby its first meal of milk.

"It doesn't know how good fresh water weeds taste," said Tanto in a whisper.

After a while, the elephant mother got to her feet. She waved to Tanto. Then she picked up the calf in the gentle curve of her trunk. She tucked it tenderly under her chin and walked softly into the woods. The other elephants followed, Tanto and Auntie with the rest.

"It can't even walk much by itself," Tanto whispered to his auntie.

"No," said Auntie, "for several months it will mainly eat and sleep."

"I'm glad I'm not a baby any more," said Tanto. "I can slide down river banks and march in single file and tear my own leafy branches off the trees. When Mother hears all we did today, I guess she'll be very proud of me."

"Yes, she will," said Auntie, stroking Tanto's shoulders with the tip of her trunk. "The old leader of the herd will be proud of you, too. And I am proud of you."

Now night had fallen over Tanto's jungle. Stars burned like small sizzling flames in the dark sky, and a breeze sighed and crackled through the trees. Tanto joined a couple of other elephant youngsters who were milling about before settling down to sleep.

"My mother had a new baby," Tanto said with pride. "I guess it's a nice one as babies go. But it just eats and sleeps. That's all it can do. I'm glad I'm growing up."

Then Tanto rolled over on his side and, yawning politely behind his trunk, he fell asleep.

Elephants as Builders

SOME ANIMALS use tools to do work. The sea otter holds a rock in its forepaws to crack open crab shells. Some monkeys and apes use sticks as tools in getting food. An elephant may use sticks as weapons if it is angry. But in doing most of its work, the elephant just uses its own huge steamroller body.

Without really intending to, elephants turn patches of tangled brush into open grasslands that can feed herds of animals. What the elephants do is tear up, for food, groves of thornbush and other small trees. They tear up some trees by curling their trunks around them and pulling. Others they tip over by leaning their broad foreheads against them and pushing. In either case, the roots are left reaching out into empty air, and the tree or bush dies.

Small animals and insects help clear away the scattered wood as it decays on the ground. Often a brush fire does part of the clearing. Soon grass begins to grow from the rich soil. Antelopes, zebra and other plant–eating animals move in to crop the young green stalks.

After some years small seedling trees begin to poke up through the grass again, and a new grove starts to grow. But for many years the grazing animals have a nice green pasture, thanks to the elephants.

Animals need water as well as food, and elephants build water holes, too. When they find a spot where there is water close to the surface under sandy soil, they tramp about, digging holes with their heavy feet. The holes soon fill with water, and other animals too can then enjoy a good drink on a hot, dry day, thanks to the work of the elephants.

Elephants also like to roll in the mud. For this sport all they need is a low spot in the ground where some water is standing after a rain. Before the water soaks into the soil, the elephants lie down and roll. All those tons of weight harden the soil beneath them until it is almost as water-tight as the bottom of a swimming pool. When the next rain comes, this elephant saucer holds water very well. Again other animals enjoy a new watering spot built by the elephants.

It is easy for other animals to find these pools, because elephants are road builders, too. An elephant herd marching through the brush clears a wide and smooth-packed trail. An elephant track is not only straight and smooth; it is almost certain to take the shortest route from one water hole to the next.

Men have managed to teach some elephants in Asia to work for them. But the elephants of Africa work freely for themselves, both building and tearing down.

Hippy Hippo's Longest Day

Young Hippy Hippopotamus's worst and longest day did not even start like other days. Most early mornings found Hippy and his mother waddling home from a midnight lunch of grass.

Home was a pool of nice, muddy water where Hippy and his mother and their friends spent their days. They liked the feel of the water sloshing against their skins while the sun blazed hot up above. They liked rubbing against one another's leathery sides and leaning their big chins on one another's backs. It was a good thing that they did like being close together, because the pool was not very large for the number of big gray bulging hippopotamuses who called it home.

The pool was not very large at best. But at the beginning of Hippy Hippo's longest day that pool was far from being at its best.

For a long time there had been no rain. The sun was pulling water from the pool every day up to the clouds. More water was soaking down into the ground. With no rain falling to refill it, the pool was almost dry.

Usually the hippos shared their water hole with many other animals. A herd of elephants marched down to drink almost every afternoon. Plump zebras trotted down in groups. And slender antelopes came bounding gracefully across the grassy plain.

Lately, though, most of these animals had wandered away. They had followed their own mysterious paths—or the wide, straight elephant trails—through the tangled brush and across the open grasslands to greener grass and water holes that were better filled.

The hippos had worried about their drying pool, but it was hard for them to decide to leave. They were slow walkers. They could not travel far in a night. And they could not be happy through a long, hot day without water in which to soak. How could they be

129

sure of finding another water hole just one night's waddle away?

That was the hippos' problem. And while they thought about it, turning long, slow thoughts over in their minds as they munched the drying grass in long, slow chomping chews, they stayed close to their old water hole as it slowly dried away.

On the morning of Hippy Hippo's longest day, Mother Hippo seemed worried as she looked out over the pool. The water no longer sloshed softly against the banks. Only a little water lay out in the middle of the pool. The rest was just a bed of red-brown squishy mud.

Mother Hippo nudged Hippy away from the mud. She edged away herself. But young Hippy was tired and thirsty and a little bit cross. He had been waddling after his mother for hours, munching dry, tasteless, trampled grass. He was tired of walking, tired of all the weight of his round tubby frame on his feet. He wanted to splash out into the water hole and let the nice cool water hold him up while he took a long delicious drink. So he pushed past his mother and, with a happy little roar, plunged into the muddy pool.

Squish—squash—squwump! The mud rose higher and higher with each step Hippy took. At the first step he sank to his stumpy ankles, at the second to the middle of his short legs. Soon the mud rose up around his plump tummy—*squash, squish, squwump!*

Poor Hippy Hippo! Before he had even reached the puddle of water that remained, he was firmly trapped in the mud.

This was nothing like the cool, delicious water he liked to drink and lie down in. This mud was a heavy weight that clung to his legs and pressed against his shoulders and held him fast.

Hippy lifted his chin and opened his mouth wide and let out his loudest roar. He thought his mother would come running and make

130

everything all right. But his mother did not come.

Mrs. Hippo knew the danger of the mud. She knew if she went to the aid of young Hippy she would soon be stuck there too. She waddled unhappily up and down the bank. She grunted and groaned and roared. But as to freeing her child from the mud, she did not know what to do.

The sun rose higher and higher above the grasslands and the drying water hole. Its rays burned hotter and hotter. It sucked the last drops of water from the surface of the mud and left it cracking dry. It dried young Hippy's tough coat until his skin itched like fire. It burned Mother Hippo's skin too. She longed to waddle away from there as fast as she could, to find another water hole. But she could not leave young Hippy behind.

When the sun was straight overhead and so hot that it had faded all the blue from the sky, young Hippy's grunts and roars died away to faint moans. He felt too bad even to make much noise any more. It was noon of the worst and longest day Hippy Hippo had ever known.

Nearby, Mrs. Hippo still stood guard. She called out to Hippy now and then. But her voice was weaker, too.

Soon the sun began slipping slowly down the sky, but its heat still blazed and burned. It was midafternoon when Mrs. Hippopotamus stiffened suddenly, her small ears cocked. She had heard a strange, unfamiliar sound.

It was the noisy motor of a powerful four-wheel-drive truck that Mother Hippo heard. *Chug-a-rum-rum-rum* it came grinding across the bumpy land. In the cab of the truck were two young men whose work it was to look after wild animals.

"There's another drying water hole over this way," one of the men was saying. "We'd better check it."

So down an elephant trail through the brush they chugged to the sun-baked pool.

There they found Mother Hippo, head down, her little eyes red and worried. She was ready to fight to keep the strangers from harming young Hippy. She could not know that the men had come to help.

Beyond Mother Hippo's big gray bulk the men could see young Hippy, half sunk in the dry, sun-cracked mud.

"This must be the young one's mother," said the man beside the driver. "Guess we'll have to put her to sleep before we can get the young one out."

The driver coasted as close as he could get to Mother Hippo. Then the second young man took his special gun from its case. He fitted into it a tranquilizing dart with enough medicine in it to put a great big mother hippopotamus to sleep for several hours. Then he aimed his gun and—*ping!*—the dart landed in Mother Hippo's shoulder.

Mother Hippo felt a sting like the bite of an insect. She shrugged her shoulder and grunted a little. Then she began to feel strange. She took a couple of uncertain steps and sagged to the ground, fast asleep.

Now the young man hopped down from the truck. He walked around Mother Hippo to the edge of the mudhole and aimed his gun at young Hippy. *Ping!* Another dart landed, this one in Hippy's shoulder.

Both young men went swiftly to work. They brought planks of wood from the back of the truck and laid them on the surface of the mud. One man took a careful step on the first plank, then another. Yes, the planks upheld his weight. With a coil of rope over his shoulder, he walked carefully out to Hippy.

He looped the rope around that young hippopotamus. Then, just as carefully, he stepped back to the bank of the mudhole with the other end of the coil of rope still in his hands.

He fastened the rope with a good strong knot to the front bumper of the truck. The driver put the truck into reverse gear. *Chug-a-r-r-r.* Slowly and carefully the driver backed the truck along the elephant trail. The long rope tightened and stretched. Would it hold?

The truck motor groaned. The rope shivered. Then slowly, slowly, the sleeping young hippopotamus was dragged from the pool. Soon, caked with mud from head to toe, he lay on the grassy bank, still asleep.

"Quick now!" called the driver. "We haven't much time."

Of course, Hippy and his mother never knew how they were hoisted into the big back of the truck. And they slept through the whole bouncy ride, too. By the time Mrs. Hippo began to stir and grunt, the driver was steering his big truck alongside a river, miles away, where plenty of water still flowed.

The man with the gun opened the back of the truck. He fixed a ramp from the truck to the ground. Then he scrambled out of sight as Mrs. Hippo awoke and pulled herself to her feet with an uneasy grunt.

She did not know where she was, of course. But she saw Hippy at her side. She nudged him and mumbled in his ear. He stirred and grunted sleepily. Mother Hippo nudged him again, harder this time. He woke up as his mother pushed him toward the slide that led down from the truck. Young Hippy almost rolled to the ground, with his mother lumbering at his heels.

She sniffed the air and squinted all around. This was not a place she knew, but she smelled water nearby. Nudging young Hippy along ahead of her, she started for the river.

Soon, with two big splashes that sent waves high up the banks, Hippy and his mother were out in the water, rolling happily this way and that. They scarcely heard the truck roar away.

By now the sun was sinking behind the flat-topped thorn trees. It was nearly time for Hippy and his mother to think about waddling ashore to scout their new home for some tasty leaves and grass. But for a little while longer they stayed in the darkening river, with the lovely cool water dancing against their sunburned skin. Young Hippy leaned his big chin against his mother's round side and opened his mouth in a huge and happy yawn. His longest day was over. And it had a happy end.

Jet Jaguar Meets His Match

JET JAGUAR awoke from his nap feeling well pleased with himself.

"I am the handsomest jaguar in all the forest," he said to himself, grunting deep in his throat.

That was very likely true. Certainly when Jet Jaguar yawned and stretched, his black velvet coat rippled over his sleek muscles in a most elegant way.

Most of the jaguars of the forest wore fur of tawny yellow-tan. They took pride in the large black rosettes scattered over their coats. They told themselves that one could scarcely see the rosettes on Jet's dark fur. But most of them secretly envied him his velvety blackness that could lose itself so quickly in the rain forest shadows. They admired the golden fire in his yellow eyes that flashed like stars in a black sky. Yes, Jet Jaguar was handsome indeed.

"I am the best hunter in all the forest, too," said Jet Jaguar to himself. Now, when People boast about themselves, they are often talking just to make themselves feel better. But what Jet Jaguar said about his hunting was very likely true.

Few of the jaguars in the forest were as big as Jet, who stretched eight feet long from nose to tail. And big or small, there were few who could match him for speed or strength or power.

Most jaguars can climb trees; but Jet could climb a smooth tree trunk, clinging with his sharp claws, so swiftly and silently that he could pounce upon sleeping parrots or a band of monkeys without even causing a stir. Or he could lie as still as a stone on a dark branch, waiting to leap from above on some passing prey.

He could sink his white fangs into a plump wild pig or break the back of a tough old crocodile he found dozing in the sunshine beside a forest pool.

He could swim the widest forest stream, scout out the covered-over nest where a turtle had buried her round white eggs, or lie on a log overhanging brown water and scoop out fish with his paw.

It was no wonder that Jet Jaguar had grown to be a giant of the forest, barrel-chested and hard-muscled, though he was still young. He got plenty of exercise and he always had plenty to eat.

It seemed that there was nothing that could trouble Jet Jaguar, no creature that could stand up to him. But one day he met his match.

He had swum the wide brown river to

hunt on its far shore. There he made a good meal of the wild pigs called peccaries. After his meal, he found a pleasant spot of deep black shade under a tangle of wide-leaved bushes, where he could enjoy a nap.

When he awoke, rested and well-fed, Jet Jaguar was ready for fun. He slithered through the forest shadows, soft-footed for all his size. And as he went he grunted softly to himself, deep in his throat.

He was out of his usual territory now, in a part of the forest new to him. Soon, through the trees ahead, he could see sunlight shining golden-green. That meant a clearing of some size.

Then he began to smell strange fragrances. Jet Jaguar lifted his blunt head and sniffed deeply. There were animals near that he had never smelled before. This was interesting.

Silently Jet pushed forward through the shadows. At the edge of the clearing he stopped short.

On a grassy ground two small brown-skinned children were playing. With arms outstretched they ran about, shouting for joy. Whenever they met and touched hands, they leaped into the air, as high as they could leap.

It was not long since Jet Jaguar had been a youngster himself. He remembered the fun of romping with his brother. This looked like a glorious game, and Jet was in the mood for play. So out into the clearing Jet Jaguar bounded to join the children at their game.

The children were amazed. They had never

seen anything like this huge, graceful creature that bounded about them. They stood as still as statues, open-mouthed, watching Jet Jaguar.

This was not what Jet wanted. He wanted them to go on running and leaping with him. He leaped and turned and leaped again. But he could not make the children understand. They just watched him and did not move.

Closer and closer came Jet in his circling.

At last, to draw the children into the game, he brushed his shoulder lightly against the younger child. The little one tumbled to the ground with a cry of surprise. Then, carefully pulling in his sharp claws, Jet tapped the older child softly.

It was just then that their mother, hearing her younger child's startled cry, stepped to the door of their small hut. To her horror she saw a huge black jaguar, its yellow eyes flashing from a dark and fearsome face, raise a paw to the older child. She was sure it planned to eat them both!

As the mother stood for half a moment with her hands at her mouth, the older child picked up a stick and struck the huge cat a blow on the head, in return for Jet's "light tap."

Jet was astonished. He had wanted the child to leap into the air, shouting with joy at his touch. Instead, he felt a sharp pain above his eyes. He, Jet Jaguar, who wanted only to join in the game, had been attacked by this small furless creature!

In a flash he turned and bounded from the clearing into the dimness of the forest where everyone knew and honored him.

Behind him the mother rushed from the hut and scooped up her baby in one arm. With the other hand she snatched at the older child, and she hurried them both into the hut.

All day she worried, but the jaguar did not reappear.

She could not have dreamed that Jet Jaguar was slinking home through the forest, mumbling softly deep in his throat.

There was no gleam in his yellow eyes now, no proud spring to his step. For Jet Jaguar, handsomest creature of the forest, swiftest and strongest of all the hunters, had met his match at last.

Note: A man who studied the animals of the rain forest for many years assures us that this story actually happened. Jaguars in their home forest will rarely attack people. But they do have a great curiosity about our strange human ways.

135

Gray Gibbon's First Flight

THROUGH THE DARK of night the gibbon family slept snug and safe on the branches of their green tree home. But when the first light of day outlined the leaves, Mother Gibbon stirred and woke.

"Morning! Morning!," she called in her fresh, sweet voice.

Small Gray Gibbon stirred and rubbed his sleepy eyes. He was curled up in a warm ball and hated to stir. But the whole family was bustling about. All except old Granddaddy Gibbon were ready to go. So small Gray Gibbon scampered along the tree branch to join his mother for the short climb.

Mother led the way, as she did every morning. Gray Gibbon followed close behind. Up they went, circling the tree trunk with their arms, climbing with their legs nearly straight.

After Gray Gibbon came his older brother. Then came his father at the end of the line.

Granddaddy Gibbon was too bent and weak to make the climb. But he watched the family wistfully until they disappeared from sight among the higher branches of the forest trees.

Soon they were out in the full early sunshine of the world at the tops of the trees. Gray Gibbon blinked his big eyes at the bright light. Then he sat down on a high branch beside his mother, clinging to the bark with both hands. He rested his chin on his upraised knees and waited. It was not a long wait. Almost at once his mother lifted her face in its white fur ruff to the sky and began to sing.

One by one the others joined in—Father with his great booming tones, Brother with middle-sized booms, Gray Gibbon's voice small and shrill. He had learned by now to carry the tune, and the notes rang out, higher and higher, in praise of the dawn and of their treetop home.

136

From distant trees the voices of unseen gibbon families floated back. All around the forest, gibbons were singing, though not, of course, in clear words:

This is our home,
this green and lovely world.
These trees grow fruits
and green leaves to feed us.
Their branches give us shelter.
And in the morning
as we watch the light return
we are glad
that this is our home, our own,
that this bit of the forest is ours.

Each gibbon family was singing of its own home, its own special place in the forest. Each family liked its own territory best. They knew every pathway through the high branches. The pathways changed as new leafy twigs pushed out from the boughs, blocking some flyways and extending others, but the gibbons knew them all.

The gibbons, you see, did not always move about by climbing up and down the trunks of trees. Most of the time they traveled by flying through the air in long, graceful leaps from branch to branch. At least the older gibbons did. Small Gray Gibbon had not yet learned to fly.

After the morning song he followed his mother down to the ground for breakfast. Breakfast was fresh-caught grasshoppers. The rule was that everyone caught his own, even Gray Gibbon. Now and then, though, his mother held a tidbit out to him in her long, slim fingers.

Gray liked the grasshopper hunting time, because then he felt nearly as grown-up as the rest. The whole family ran about, close to the base of their home tree. They ran lightly on their hind feet, searching with out-stretched arms for lively insects to eat.

Gray Gibbon had a lovely time. He hunted under green leaves, surprising small lizards. He popped out from behind tree trunks, surprising his big brother. Gray would have liked to go on nibbling and playing, but Father Gibbon soon called a halt.

At Father Gibbon's word, everyone hunted a last grasshopper or two. These they did not eat. They carried them carefully between thumb and finger as they climbed back up to their home branches. There Granddaddy Gibbon waited patiently for breakfast to be brought to him.

Soon after breakfast, Father and Big Brother Gibbon set out for their day's work. Their work was not only to find food but to check the boundaries of their home territory to make certain that no other gibbons strayed into it.

"I will be glad when you can come with me again," Father Gibbon said to Mother Gibbon when it was time for him to leave.

"So will I," said Mother Gibbon. "As soon as young Gray here learns to fly, we will both come with you." She smiled down at small Gray Gibbon and fondled his coat of short silky fur with her gentle fingers.

"You lead the way this morning, son," said Father to Big Brother.

Big Brother smiled and nodded. Then, spreading his long thin arms, he sailed out into the air from the high home branch. With his right hand he caught hold of a branch of the next big tree; swinging it behind him, he sailed on to another branch which he caught in his left hand. A graceful push sent him on to a third. And behind him his father swished through the air, following the trail he set, hand for hand.

Gray Gibbon followed them with his eyes as long as he could. How he longed to fly with them! He had heard such tales of the splendid trees where the figs and mangosteens,

sturdy branch caught him. By the time he landed, his mother was beside him, wrapping him in her warm arms and comforting him.

Soon they were back at the home place. Mother Gibbon gave Gray some lunch, and then cleaned his fur. "After your nap," she promised, "we'll have a flying lesson. You already know how it should go. What you need is practice at some of the tricks." As she spoke she was smoothing the tangles in Gray's coat, removing bits of dirt and tree bark, stroking and smoothing the short fur until it shone.

Gray liked this. He lolled against his mother's knee, half asleep. But Granddaddy Gibbon was grumbling from his place against the tree trunk.

"Child that age should be on his own," Granddaddy said. "He's big enough to know his way through the trees. At his age I could make the rounds of our home territory as well as my dad."

Mother Gibbon smiled. She knew that Granddaddy wanted some attention too. So she told young Gray to play by himself, and she turned to clean and groom Granddaddy's fur with her light finger strokes.

As she looked more closely at Granddaddy, though, Mother Gibbon's smile faded. He was shivering. His grumble had changed to a hacking cough. Granddaddy was really ill.

"If only your father would come home," said Mother to Gray. She tilted her head to one side, listening. Not a sound of Father and Big Brother could she hear. She sat very still, looking off into the forest as far as she could look. Not a glimpse of Father and Big Brother could she see.

"If only I had some of those special leaves," moaned Granddaddy, still shivering all over his thin, bent frame.

Gray Gibbon knew the leaves Granddaddy meant. Mother had fed them to him when he

bananas and tamarind pods grew. He had not been there since he was a baby, clinging to his mother's fur. He wanted so much to see them again for himself.

At the thought, Gray flung out his small arms and leaped from his safe branch toward a leafy twig not far away. His heart seemed to be in his throat as he sailed, flat as a sailing leaf, across the space. Then his fingers gripped the twig in a firm hold.

Gray had not looked ahead, though, to choose a second handhold. He had not looked below to find a resting place for his hind feet. He snatched at the small twig with both hands—and under his weight it broke!

Down went Gray, through a net of green leaves. He did not have far to fall before a

138

did not feel well. He knew where the tree was. Mother had taken him there when he was still small enough so she could fly through the air while he clung to her fur. That tree was not far away.

Mother was busy now, stroking Granddaddy's fur and holding one of his thin old hands in hers. Father and Big Brother were still somewhere far away. It was up to young Gray, he decided, to get those healing leaves.

Gray walked out along the home bough, balancing with care. He was looking for good hand holds off in the forest. When he had spotted a couple, he took a deep breath. Then he spread his arms wide and dove out into green space.

His left hand opened, and the first branch fitted neatly into the circle of fingers and thumb. Thrusting it behind him, he swung on, out into open air again, his right hand reaching for the next branch. He caught it neatly, and the rhythm of his leaps sent him swinging smoothly on across the forest.

Gray Gibbon soon reached the tree with the special healing leaves. But what was this? There were other gibbons, strangers, sitting on the branches, nibbling at the tender leaves. They were on the home territory of Gray's own family. This was not right!

Gray knew what his father would do. He was his father's son. So he landed on a sturdy bough, stood up to his full height, and, swinging his arms, he let out a shrill yell.

The other gibbons were surprised. They yelled back. Then they came to see who was there. When they saw small Gray Gibbon all alone, they were amazed. Surely, they thought, it would not take much to frighten him away. So the three intruders stood side by side and they all yelled together at Gray.

He was frightened. His heart pounded in his small chest. But he knew this was his family's tree. And he had to gather the leaves for Granddaddy. So he yelled back in his small, shrill voice.

Not far away, Father and Big Brother sat on a smooth, pale branch of their favorite fig tree, eating ripe figs. They heard the yells. At once they were on their feet. Then up the fig tree they climbed to its highest branch. And out across the forest spaces they sailed, hand over hand, until they reached the tree where young Gray Gibbon all alone was defending the family's territory.

They added their yells to Gray's small shrill one. Father Gibbon's bellow was as loud as those of any two men. Big Brother's was loud, too, and also angry, because he knew he and his family were in the right.

The other gibbons knew well enough that they were in the wrong. They knew this tree was not in their territory. So they slipped to the ground without a fight.

Father and Big Brother followed them to the edge of their territory, still shouting as they went. But the anger was gone from their voices now. They knew that they had won.

Meanwhile, back in the special tree, young Gray Gibbon had picked a handful of the healing leaves. But once he had picked them, his legs gave way. He sat down on a tree bough and clung there with both arms. All at once he knew that he was too tired to make his way back home.

That was where Father and Big Brother found him, hunched on the bough with his head between his knees.

When he heard them coming, Gray looked up, his big eyes worried. "I know I shouldn't have come so far," he said. "But Granddaddy was sick and needed these leaves. Mother couldn't leave him alone. So I came. And now I—I—" Young Gray could not go on.

"You've done just fine," said Father, his booming voice softer now. "Take a good hold and I'll give you a ride home."

So home went young Gray Gibbon, gliding through the air, clinging to his father's fur.

His mother heard the snap and crackle of the branches as they drew near. She came running along the home bough to meet them.

"I've been worried sick," she said.

Father let young Gray down, and Mother snatched him up in her long arms.

"I've brought Granddaddy the healing leaves," Gray said. The leaves were crushed and crumpled, but there they were, still smelling spicy, clutched in Gray's small palm.

"Take them to Granddaddy," said his mother. And away ran Gray. Then Mother turned to Father with outstretched arms and a smile of welcome.

"Our baby is growing up," she said. "He has learned to help others."

"He has learned to stand up for the family, too," said Father proudly as he took Mother in his arms.

"And," said Big Brother, looking on, "he has learned to fly."

Note: "A man's home is his castle," people say. They mean that a man will defend the place he has chosen for his family's home. This is not true of man alone. Most animals have a strong built-in feeling about their homes.

Fish swim thousands of miles to lay their eggs in the same spot where they started their own lives. Birds, after long journeys across trackless skies, return to the same marsh or woodland, often to the same tree.

A few animals like elephants that must keep wandering to find enough to eat do not have a strong feeling about their homes; but most, like the gibbons and their cousins the monkeys and apes, mark off their own home territories and defend them—with heaps of twigs, dabs of scent, drumming on the chest —or with morning song.